THE SYMPHONIES
FOR ORGAN

RECENT RESEARCHES IN THE MUSIC OF THE NINETEENTH AND EARLY TWENTIETH CENTURIES

Rufus Hallmark, general editor

A-R Editions, Inc., publishes seven series of musicological editions
that present music brought to light in the course of current research:

Recent Researches in the Music of the Middle Ages and Early Renaissance
Charles Atkinson, general editor

Recent Researches in the Music of the Renaissance
James Haar, general editor

Recent Researches in the Music of the Baroque Era
Christoph Wolff, general editor

Recent Researches in the Music of the Classical Era
Eugene K. Wolf, general editor

Recent Researches in the Music of the Nineteenth and Early Twentieth Centuries
Rufus Hallmark, general editor

Recent Researches in American Music
H. Wiley Hitchcock, general editor

Recent Researches in the Oral Traditions of Music
Philip V. Bohlman, general editor

Each *Recent Researches* edition is devoted to works
by a single composer or to a single genre of composition.
The contents are chosen for their potential interest to scholars
and performers, then prepared for publication according to the
standards that govern the making of all reliable historical editions.

Subscribers to any of these series, as well as patrons of subscribing institutions,
are invited to apply for information about the "Copyright-Sharing Policy"
of A-R Editions, Inc., under which policy any part of an edition
may be reproduced free of charge for study or performance.

For information contact

A-R EDITIONS, INC.
801 Deming Way
Madison, Wisconsin 53717

(608) 836-9000

RECENT RESEARCHES IN THE MUSIC OF THE NINETEENTH
AND EARLY TWENTIETH CENTURIES • VOLUME 16

Charles-Marie Widor

THE SYMPHONIES FOR ORGAN

Symphonie VI

Edited by John R. Near

A-R Editions, Inc.
Madison

Charles-Marie Widor
THE SYMPHONIES FOR ORGAN

Edited by John R. Near

Recent Researches in the Music
of the Nineteenth and Early Twentieth Centuries

Opus 13	Symphonie I	in C Minor	Volume 11
	Symphonie II	in D Major	Volume 12
	Symphonie III	in E Minor	Volume 13
	Symphonie IV	in F Minor	Volume 14
Opus 42	Symphonie V	in F Minor	Volume 15
	Symphonie VI	in G Minor	Volume 16
	Symphonie VII	in A Minor	Volume 17
	Symphonie VIII	in B Major	Volume 18
Opus 70	*Symphonie gothique*		Volume 19
Opus 73	*Symphonie romane*		Volume 20

© 1993 by A-R Editions, Inc.
All rights reserved
Printed in the United States of America

Library of Congress Cataloging-in-Publication Data

Widor, Charles Marie, 1844–1937.
   [Symphonies, organ, no. 6, op. 42, no. 2, G minor]
   Symphonie VI / Charles-Marie Widor ; edited by John R. Near.
   p. of music. —(The symphonies for organ / Charles-Marie Widor)
(Recent researches in the music of the nineteenth and early
twentieth centuries, ISSN 0193-5364 ; v. 16)
   "The original French editions and copies of these with corrections
and emendations in Widor's hand form the basis for this critical
edition"—p. vii.
   ISBN 0-89579-284-2
   1. Symphonies (Organ)   I. Near, John Richard, 1947–   .
II. Series.   III. Series: Widor, Charles Marie, 1844–1937.
Symphonies, organ (A-R Editions)
M2.R23834   vol. 16
[M8]   93-719287
                                       CIP
                                       M

Contents

Introduction
   The Sources   vii
   Editorial Policies   viii
   Widor's Registrations   ix
   Critical Commentary   ix

Widor's *Avant-propos*   xvi

Symphonie VI in G Minor
   I   3
   II   20
   III. Intermezzo   26
   IV   39
   V. Finale   45

Appendix 1
   I. Edition *A'*, Versions *B/B'* and *C'/D*, Mm. 123–31   57

Appendix 2
   III. Intermezzo. Edition *A'*, Mm. 81–100, 253–73   58

Appendix 3
   III. Intermezzo. Edition *B*, Mm. 81–100, 253–73   59

Appendix 4
   III. Intermezzo. Version *C'/D*, Mm. 87–96, 259–68   61

Widor as he appears on a card (original dimensions: 4 cm. × 7.5 cm.) issued by the firm of Félix Potin—probably in the late 1890s—as one in a series of hundreds of portraits of famous persons in the arts, the armed services, and politics. The same portrait appears in the American periodical *Music* 17/2 (Dec. 1899), 187.

Introduction

From the time of their first publication, the organ symphonies of Charles-Marie Widor (1844–1937) have been recognized as masterpieces. Their influence on subsequent organ literature was once immense. As new generations of organ music became popular, however, there inevitably came a time when Widor's symphonies were neglected, often being judged outmoded. Even the French Romantic organ, perfected by Cavaillé-Coll and adored by musicians, was abused by later generations. Sufficient time was required to pass before Widor's art and instrument could be considered from a fresh and independent musical perspective. That perspective has evidently been achieved, for in recent years increasing numbers of musicians have begun evaluating the symphonies on their own terms, with the result that the works have enjoyed a notable resurgence of popularity. At the same time, the French Romantic organ has regained its former status.

Widor was perhaps his own most demanding critic. Following the first publication of each organ symphony, a continual transformation was effected by the composer through several revisions. In certain cases nearly six decades intervened between first and last versions of a work. Even after the final published edition, Widor continued to scrutinize his organ works, applying finishing touches to the pieces that have constituted his most enduring legacy.

This comprehensive edition of Widor's ten organ symphonies is the first to incorporate the many final emendations made by the composer in his own copies. Here also are presented for the first time together substantially or completely different earlier versions of passages, sections, and complete movements as they were conceived by Widor in the course of his long career. Using information in the Critical Commentary and the music of the Appendixes, musicians can perform or study these several earlier versions of each work.

The Preface to this edition (vol. 11, Symphonie I) provides a full discussion of the symphonies' genesis and historical environment as well as an extended discussion of editorial policy, sources, and performance. In this Introduction are provided information on performance sufficient to give the reader a sense of Widor's own preferences in registration and expression (including a translation of his foreword, or *avant-propos*), a conspectus of the sources, a summary of editorial policy, and a Critical Commentary.

The Sources

The original French editions and copies of these with corrections and emendations in Widor's hand form the basis for this critical edition. The locations of Widor's original holographs, if extant, are unknown. After extensively researching these works, the editor believes that all editions have surfaced, with one possible exception, noted in the Preface. These are listed here together with the identifying abbreviations used in the Critical Commentary and Appendixes. (More complete information on the sources appears in the Preface to the present edition.)

A   The first edition of opus 13, Symphonies I–IV, published in Paris in 1872 by the firm of J. Maho.

A'   A subsequent issue of *A* with minuscule alterations, published in 1879 by the firm of J. Hamelle together with the first editions of Symphonies V and VI.

B   The first complete issue of opus 42, comprising Symphonies V–VIII, together with the first major revision of opus 13, published in Paris in 1887 by Hamelle.

B'   A subsequent issue of *B* with small revisions to Symphonies I, VI, VII, and VIII, released between 1888 and 1892.

C   A new edition of opuses 13 and 42 (excepting Symphonie VI), published in 1901 and bearing the heading "New edition, revised, and entirely modified by the composer (1900–1901)."

C'   A subsequent issue of *C* that includes a new version of Symphonie VI and revisions to Symphonies I–V and VII–VIII, released by 1911.

D   A new edition of opuses 13 and 42, published in 1920, bearing the heading "New edition, revised, and entirely modified by the composer (1914–1918), (1920)."

E   The final published edition, again with revisions, issued 1928–29.

Emend 1   A copy of *B'* apparently used by Widor while preparing the revisions of edition *C* but also containing other emendations.

Emend 2   A bound and complete collection of single symphonies (representing variously the versions of editions *D* or *E*) with emendations made by Widor mostly after 1929, the year of edition *E*.

Emend 3   A copy of Symphonie V in the version of edition *D*, with numerous emendations by the composer, dated October 1927 in Widor's hand. This copy includes the revisions present in the 1929 edition, but it also contains further emendations, including some duplicated in *Emend* 2 and arguably entered after 1929.

Schw 5–7 Gunsbach, France, Maison Schweitzer, MO 157, a bound volume of Symphonies V, VI (movement V), and VII (movements I–IV). On the first page of Symphonie V, Schweitzer has signed his name and written, "Cet exemplaire est corrigé à la main par Widor même pour moi" [This copy is corrected in Widor's own hand for me]. These copies represent edition C, except for Symphonie VI (movement V), which, judging from *Schw* 6a, represents edition B'.

Schw 6a Gunsbach, France, Maison Schweitzer, MO 159, comprises Symphonie VI (movements I–IV), which has been removed from MO 157. This copy represents edition B'.

Schw 6b Gunsbach, France, Maison Schweitzer, MO 162, comprises a loose copy of Symphonie VI, movement IV, edition undetermined.

Riem 6 Berea, Ohio, The Riemenschneider Bach Institute at Baldwin-Wallace College, R 3995, comprises a single copy of Symphonie VI in edition D.

Identical versions of movements in different editions are denoted in the Critical Commentary and the Appendixes by a slash between the identifying letters; for example, A/A'/B/B' means that a movement so identified remains the same through editions A, A', B, and B'.

Editorial Policies

Edition E (or, what amounts to the same thing, a version remaining constant through edition E) is generally taken as the principal source for the main body of this edition. Sources for Appendix variants are identified individually in the Critical Commentary. All departures from the source either are distinguished typographically (when they are editorial and straightforward) or are identified in the Critical Commentary (when they derive from other sources or are not explained by policies described here). There are two exceptions to the policy of bracketing: editorial ties, slurs, hairpins, and directs are dashed; editorial cautionary accidentals appear in reduced size; all other editorial additions are enclosed in brackets.

The original French prints are themselves replete with cautionary accidentals, usually provided to cancel flats and sharps in previous measures. All except repetitious cautionary accidentals within a measure are preserved in this edition.

In the Critical Commentary the three staves of a system are indexed 1, 2, and 3, in order from top to bottom. Occasionally staff 1 in the source editions is congested, while an empty or nearly empty staff lies directly below. In such contexts this edition sometimes tacitly transfers left-hand voices to the open staff 2.

In the sources, indications of dynamics under staff 1 are sometimes duplicated under staves 2 or 3 or both in contexts where the Pédale and other manuals would have to share those dynamics in any event. The editor has suppressed most of these redundant dynamic indications. In addition, the old engravings frequently place dynamic indications over staff 1 because of space limitations on the page; conversely, they sometimes place tempo indications between staves 1 and 2 for the same reason. This edition tacitly regularizes the position of all such marks, putting dynamic indications within the system and tempo indications above it. There is an obvious exception to this rule: namely, when a dynamic is meant to apply to one staff alone, it appears closest to the affected voice(s)—therefore, sometimes above staff 1. Because Widor indicated registration and dynamics somewhat differently in editions A and A', the source placement of the relevant signs is preserved in appendix extracts from them.

Widor indicated staccato with the dot up to the late 1890s, but he favored the wedge thereafter. The two signs become mixed in passages partially revised by the composer after about 1900 (the period of edition C). Widor's pedagogical works on organ music reveal that both signs had the same significance for him. In the present edition all wedges are tacitly changed to dots in pieces conceived before Widor's change of orthography; wedges are retained in movements composed after the change.

Beaming in the original French editions is sometimes used to clarify phrasing. Beaming in the new edition follows that of the sources except when, under certain stringent conditions spelled out in detail in the Preface to this edition (see vol. 11, Symphonie I), it can be shown with great probability that inconsistencies arise through oversight or through adherence to an outmoded convention for beaming.

Characteristic of Widor's musical orthography is its attention to inner contrapuntal voices in every musical texture. At times this leads to a phalanx of stems all aiming for the same metrical position. Stemming in the new edition generally follows that of the sources, since the appearance of counterpoint, even in predominantly homophonic textures, conveys much of the "feel" and attitude proper to Widor's symphonies. Departures from the source are made only in clearly defined circumstances spelled out in detail in the Preface to this edition. In general, the number of voices in a measure is kept constant. In clearly homophonic contexts, where Widor himself is less strict, inconsistencies in the number of voices in a measure are usually allowed to stand. All editorial rests are bracketed. Stems added by analogy with parallel or closely similar passages are not bracketed, but the source reading is reported in a critical note. All other stems added to clarify inconsistent voicing are bracketed. Infrequently, superfluous rests or stems in the sources are tacitly removed to keep part writing consistent in a measure.

In conformity with accepted practice of that era, the original French editions of Widor's organ symphonies provide double barlines for all changes of key and for some changes of meter. In this edition these are converted to single barlines unless there is also a new tempo, a new texture, or some other sign of a structural subdivision.

Reference to pitch in the Critical Commentary is made as follows: middle C = c'; C above middle C = c"; C below middle C = c; two octaves below middle C = C. Successive pitches are separated by commas, simultaneous pitches by virgules.

Widor's Registrations

Widor generally indicated registrations by family of tone-color instead of exact stop nomenclature. In so doing he never intended to condone willful or indiscriminate interpretations of his registrational plans. He had a particular horror of kaleidoscopic stop changes and artlessly haphazard use of the Expression pedal. To those who indulged in a continual manipulation of the stops or Expression pedal, he habitually advised, "I beg you, no magic lantern effects." Barring the unfortunate necessity of making certain adaptations to varying organs, one should no more alter the "orchestration" of a Widor organ symphony than change or dress up the instrumentation of a Beethoven symphony. Clearly, the faithful realization of Widor's registrational plan is essential to the presentation of these works as the composer heard them. Beyond this, knowledge of the Cavaillé-Coll organ, the instrument preferred by Widor, will also prove useful to the performer intent on maximum fidelity to the composer's intention. A discussion of this organ and its constraints on performance can be found in the Preface to this edition (see vol. 11, Symphonie I).

To indicate the registration he wanted, Widor adopted a relatively simple shorthand system: **G** represents Grand-orgue (Great); **P** Positif (Positive); **R** Récit (Swell); **Péd.** Pédale (Pedal). Fonds are the foundation stops; Anches the chorus reed stops as well as all correlative stops included in the Jeux de combinaison. Pitch designations are self-evident.

When found above, within, or directly below the keyboard staves, a single letter instructs the organist to play on that particular uncoupled manual. When two or three letters are combined in these locations, the first designates the manual to play on, the second and subsequent letters what is to be coupled to it. For example, **GPR** instructs the organist to play on the Grand-orgue with the Positif and Récit coupled to it; **PR** tells one to play on the Positif with the Récit coupled to it; and so on.

When found under the lowest staff, one or more letters designate which manuals are to be coupled to the Pédale. When Widor employs only a dynamic marking in the course of the Pédale line, the performer should determine at his own discretion which Pédale coupler needs to be retired or reintroduced.

All crescendo and decrescendo indications, no matter how lengthy, are to be effected only by manipulation of the Expression pedal, unless the crescendo leads to a fff. In that case the Jeux de combinaison of each division are to be brought into play successively on strong beats: first those of the Récit (perhaps already on), then those of the Positif (sometimes indicated with a ff), and finally those of the Grand-orgue and Pédale on the fff. For the decrescendo they are to be retired in reverse order on weak beats.

Critical Commentary

Symphonies V and VI, composed only a few months apart, evince the same captivating aesthetic; these are Widor's "Waldstein" and "Appassionata." In opus 13 the composer grappled with the symphonic ideal in organ music, in opus 42 he gives it full wing, bringing the term *symphonie pour orgue* into complete parity with *symphonie pour orchestre*. Like the orchestral symphony, these organ symphonies function as integral works; it is to be regretted when selected movements are programmed singly.

Actually composed before Symphonie V, in F minor, Symphonie VI, in G minor, was premiered (with the title "5me Symphonie") by Widor in the series of inaugural concerts for the Cavaillé-Coll organ at the Trocadéro, on 24 August 1878. (For a full description of the genesis of this symphony, see First Performances and Publications in the Preface to this edition, found in vol. 11, Symphonie I.) Like the five-movement F-minor symphony, this one exhibits architectural symmetry. Widor's students often told of his comparing musical structures to architectural models. In the symmetrical ordering of movements (fast—slow—fast—slow—fast) and in their internal construction, these symphonies embody a principle that Widor exhorted his students to assimilate.

> "Of all the arts," he often affirmed, "none has more rapport with music than architecture." The art of the architect is directed towards materializing the dream in space, and giving it a form, both harmonious and solid. The art of the musician consists of raising in sonorous space an ideal construction, one that is beautiful, expressive, and very well framed. And [Widor] then took pleasure in drawing pertinent parallels between the robust builders of the medieval cathedrals and the great sonorous architects of the 18th and 19th centuries. "Go see," he sharply counseled us, "the wonderful facade of Notre Dame, and tell me if there exists something that more resembles the plan of a first movement of a symphony than the conception of this central portal, vigorously framed with its two towers like a development placed between two symmetrical wings." Music, he loved to repeat, lives from symmetries and recurrences. "Art is made of will, affirmation, logic."[*]

---

[*]Georges Favie, "Une grande figure d'éducateur, Charles-Marie Widor," *La Petite Maîtrise* 288 (May 1937): 34–35.

Widor avers in the *Avant-propos* to his symphonies (given complete in this volume):

> It is . . . clear to what extent the organ symphony differs from the orchestral symphony. No confusion is to be feared. One will never write indiscriminately for the orchestra or for the organ, but . . . one will have to exercise the same care with the combination of timbres in an organ composition as in an orchestral work.

His composition pupils also reported that Widor treated this subject insightfully from his profound understanding of both resources. Widor saw great potential in the combination of organ and orchestra. In revising Berlioz's *Grand traité d'instrumentation et d'orchestration modernes*, Widor took strong exception to the older composer's view that

> a secret antipathy seems to exist between these two powers. The Organ and the Orchestra are both kings, or rather, one is Emperor, the other Pope; . . . their interests are too vast and too diverse to allow of amalgamation.*

Widor countered:

> If Berlioz were still alive he would forswear his views of yore, or rather the views that were so unfairly instilled into his mind. Admirable new effects may yet be drawn from the union of the two former rivals, "the Emperor and the Pope," who, converted into fast allies, manifest ever growing mutual sympathy.†

Widor wrote these lines in 1904, but he had demonstrated their soundness over twenty-two years earlier.

In the G-minor organ symphony, Widor realized the new genre's orchestral potential, and within four years of its composition he borrowed the first and last movements, together with the third movement of Symphonie II, and arranged them as a *Symphonie pour orgue et orchestre*.‡ The scoring in the outer movements for full orchestra and organ contrasts with the sparer scoring for strings and organ in the second movement. In its new form the work began a life of its own. The premiere was likely in the summer of 1882, when Widor traveled to London; at Royal Albert Hall the composer was "acclaimed in performing, in the presence of the court, his symphony for organ and orchestra."§ Even after Widor composed his highly successful *Troisième symphonie* for organ and orchestra, opus 69 (1895), this earlier *arrangement* continued to be admired. Undoubtedly, its most prestigious performance occurred at its American premiere, in John Wanamaker's Philadelphia department store. On the evening of 27 March 1919, twelve thousand listeners packed the main floor and upper galleries around the grand court to hear a gala program presented by the Philadelphia Orchestra, conducted by Leopold Stokowski and with Charles Courboin at the great organ. Widor's Symphonie VI for organ and orchestra was the featured attraction.‖

I

After the Toccata from Symphonie V, this movement has attracted the attention of organists more than any other in the symphonies. It has been frequently cited as Widor's masterpiece for the instrument, but after extended study of his organ music, the editor is reluctant to rank it higher than several other superlative movements; one has to admit, however, that the music maintains an exceptional degree of grandeur and nobility. Like the first movement of Symphonie V, this Allegro is best categorized as a type of variations. The majestic, richly harmonized opening theme is contrasted by a restless, recitativelike monodic theme containing motives derived from the first theme. The two are adroitly combined in various ways throughout the development of the piece.

The movement exists in four slightly different versions: A', B/B', C'/D, and E. (This symphony appears not to have been issued in edition C; see Sources, "Edition C," p. xiv, in the Preface to this edition, found in vol. 11, Symphonie I.) For the final version, edition E is the principal source.

In this movement edition E contains several ambiguities that can only be explained by knowing the variant readings in previous versions; for instance, directives effective in an earlier reading but no longer in edition E were negligently allowed to remain in the score. Reports on the variant readings of the earlier versions are given below. Additionally, Appendix 1 gives measures 123–31, the most extended revision, in edition A' (the original reading) and versions B/B' and C'/D (representing the first revision for those measures).

---

*Charles-Marie Widor, *The Technique of the Modern Orchestra*, trans. by E. Suddard (London: J. Williams, 1906), 139.

†Ibid., 144.

‡Paris, Bibliothèque nationale, Vma Ms 603, is the first movement, Allegro maestoso, of a "Symphonie pour orgue et orchestre," opus 42[*bis*]. In the hand of a copyist, J. Faes, and dated "janvier 1904," the manuscript contains numerous additional marks and emendations in Widor's hand. The autograph is apparently lost.

Paris, Bibliothèque nationale, Ms 18135, is an autograph score of a "Symphonie d'orgue" for organ and orchestra, opus 42[*bis*], dated "3 avril 82" on the last page of the third movement. This manuscript comprises the second movement, Andante (paginated 31–39), and the third movement, Final (paginated 41–76).

Paris, Bibliothèque nationale, Vma Ms 604 and Vma Ms 605, include, variously from all three movements, a fragmentary set of orchestral parts; a second-violin part is marked for the "Royal Orchestral Society as soon as possible."

Berea, Ohio, The Riemenschneider Bach Institute at Baldwin-Wallace College, R 4011, is a manuscript score with corrections in Widor's hand, dated "16 août 27."

An edition of the *Symphonie pour orgue et orchestre*, opus 42[*bis*], will appear as a supplement to this series of the ten organ symphonies.

---

§*Musica Sacra* 7 (August 1882): 93–94.

‖See Linda L. Tyler, "'Commerce and Poetry Hand in Hand': Music in American Department Stores, 1880–1930," *Journal of the American Musicological Society* 45 (1992): 87. A copy of the program, signed by Courboin, Wanamaker, and Stokowski, was sent to Widor with an inscription in French: "To the great master, artist, and eminent composer, Charles-Marie Widor. In remembrance of the magnificent concert given in the grand court of Wanamaker's in Philadelphia, U.S.A., on the largest organ in the world (240 stops complete) with the magnificent Philadelphia Orchestra with Leopold Stokowski, conductor." (Thanks to the Widor family for making the program available to me.)

In place of the usual opening registration directives, Widor specifies all unison couplers engaged: "Grand-orgue, Positif, Récit, Pédale accouplés." Thereafter in the music itself single manual directives are used almost exclusively in all editions. Here and in most of the symphony these clearly stand as abbreviations, given in lieu of the usual complete directive, which indicates coupled manuals. In other symphonies abbreviated directives often follow a first occurrence of the full directive, and such is the case in this movement as well. The full directive **GPR** is given at measure 56, beat 4, and thereafter (mm. 69, 71, 73, 75, 76, et seq.) the source gives **G** only. In versions *A'*, *B/B'*, and *C'/D*, there are only two places (mm. 164, staff 2, and 167, staff 1) where **P** is clearly intended to stand alone (the full directive **PR** being given in m. 173, staff 1, to indicate engaging the Positif to Récit coupler—see critical report below); after Widor revised the registration for *E*, this situation was no longer present. To clarify the composer's intentions, this edition indicates **GPR** in place of the source's **G**, and **PR** in place of **P**; exceptional cases are described in the critical notes. (For further discussion of this matter, see Symphonie II, Critical Commentary, "VI. Finale," in vol. 12 of this series.)

VARIANTS IN EDITIONS A' THROUGH D

Edition *A'*, version *B/B'*, and version *C'/D* differ from the present edition as follows. The metronome mark is added in *B*. Mm. 1 and 2, staff 1 has no accents in *A'* through *D*; staff 3 has no slur extending to m. 4 in *A'* through *D*. Mm. 5 and 6, beat 4, notes are quarter notes in *A'* through *D*. Mm. 7–10, staff 3 has no slurs in *A'* through *D*. Mm. 17–20, note 1, staff-3 part doubled an octave higher in *A'* through *D*. M. 32, beat 4, directive is *quasi recitativo e à piacere* in *A'*. M. 44 has no *rit.* in *A'*. M. 45 has no *a tempo* in *A'*. M. 57, the metronome mark is added in *B*. Mm. 58, 59, 62 and 63, there are no slurs in any edition—edition follows *Emend* 2. Mm. 80–82, staff-2 part is on staff 3 (beginning d') with *pp* dynamic mark in *A'* through *D*; a registration directive under staff 3 (m. 80) reads "**Péd.** (Fonds) solo" in all editions—when the staff-3 part was transferred to staff 2 in *E*, "solo" should have been deleted from the directive. M. 83, staff 2, beat 1 has half rest (no d half note), staff 3 has d dotted half note in *A'* through *D*; beat 4, crescendo hairpin is located above staff 3 in all editions.

M. 108, staff 1, the e"[-flat] notes are tied and there is no slur from beat 2 to m. 109, beat 1, in *A'* through *D*; beat 3, e"[-flat]/c''' half notes are not tied to m. 109, beat 1, in *A'*. M. 109, staff 1, beat 1 has quarter notes, beat 2 has no manual directive (it remains **GPR**) in any edition; the e"[-flat] notes are tied and there is no slur from beat 2 to m. 110, beat 1, in *A'* through *D*. M. 113, staff 1, beat 2 has no manual directive (it remains **GPR**) in any edition. M. 117, staff 1 has no manual directive (it remains **GPR**) in any edition; beat 1, dynamic mark is *f* in *A'* through *D*. M. 121, beat 1 has *sempre cresc.* in *A'* through *D*. M. 123, staff 1, beat 1 has no manual directive (it has remained **GPR** from m. 98) in any edition. Mm. 123–31, see Appendix 1 for variant readings of edition *A'* and versions *B/B'* and *C'/D*. M. 132 has no "Large" in *A'* through *D*. M. 133, staff 1, upper voice is two b"[-flat] half notes (not tied) and the slur ends on the second b"[-flat] (which is not tied into m. 134) in *A'*. M. 134, staff 1, upper voice, there is no tie between the two b"[-flat] notes and a new slur begins on beat 3 in *A'*. M. 136, staff 1, the slur ends on beat 4 in *A'* (there is no new slur thru m. 138); the slur ends on the second half of beat 2 in *B* through *E*—this is likely an engraver's error made when the slurring was revised for *B*. M. 138 has no *rit.* or crescendo hairpin in *A'* through *D*; staves 1 and 2, beat 3 chord is dotted quarter notes, beat 4 chord is eighth notes in *A'* and *B/B'*. M. 139 has no *a tempo* in *A'* through *D*. Mm. 139–41, staves 1 and 2, beat 1, chords have no tenuto mark in *A'*. Mm. 146 and 147 have no slurs in *A'* through *D*.

M. 162, staff 1, chord 1, d' has no sharp in any edition—an error. M. 163, staff 1, beat 4, registration directives in *A'* through *D* are as follows: "**R** Hautbois et flûtes 4, 8" and "**P** Fonds de 4 et de 8." M. 164, staff 2, beat 1, manual directive is **P** in *A'* through *D*. M. 167, staff 1, beat 4, manual directive is **P** in all editions—it should have been corrected in *E* to **PR**. M. 172, staff 2, upper voice, note 6 has no sharp in any edition—an error. M. 173, staff 1, beat 2, note 2 has **PR** in all editions—this directive is only needed in *A'* through *D*. M. 175, staff 2, note 2, a registration directive reads "**G** Fonds 4, 8, 16" in all editions—edition suggests making the change for **G** at m 151. Mm. 186–88, staff 1, dyad 2 is quarter notes in *A'*—by apparent oversight, the second dyad of m. 189 remained quarter notes in all editions. Mm. 186–87, staff 3 doubles the lower note of staff 2 (beginning c-sharp) in *A'*. Mm. 188–94, staff 1, manual directives added in *C'*. M. 189, staff 1, dyad 2, upper note is f" in *Emend* 1—this emendation was never effected. M. 192, beat 1, a registration directive reads "(anches du Récit, *pp*)" in all editions—this directive should have been deleted in *E*; staff 1, dyad 4 is beamed and tied to g'/e"[-natural] eighth notes on the first half of beat 1 in m. 193 in *A'*. M. 193, staff 1, dyad 4 is beamed and tied to e'/c" eighth notes on the first half of beat 1 in m. 194 in *A'*. M. 194, staff 1, dyad 2 is quarter notes in *A'*; dyad 4 is e'/c" and is beamed and tied to e'/c" eighth notes on the first half of beat 1 in m. 195 in *A'*. Mm. 195–96, *rit.* and *a tempo* added in *B*; there is no dynamic mark in *A'* through *D*. M. 197, staff 2, beat 3, note 2 is a-flat in *A'*. M. 198, staff 1, chord is half notes; staff 2 is at rest, and staff 3 continues with staff-2 part in *A'* through *D*. M. 199 has no *rit.* in *A'*; staff 2, beats 1 and 2 are at rest, and staff 3 has staff-2 part in *A'* through *D* (note 2 is a-natural in *B/B'* and *C'/D*). M. 200 has no *a tempo* in *A'*.

Mm. 222 and 223, staff 1 has no accents and there is a slur from m. 221, beat 4, to m. 223, beat 1, in *A'* through *D*; staff 3 has no slur in *A'* through *D*. M. 223, staff 1 has no accents in *A'* through *D*. Mm. 226–27, staves 1 and 2 have no slurs in any edition. Mm. 228–29, staff 2 doubles staff-1 part an octave lower, staff 3 has staff-2 part (note 1 has no staccato dot) in *A'* through *D*. M. 232, *agitato* is not in *A'*; staff 3, beat 1 is G/g eighth notes, eighth rest; beat 2 is F/f eighth notes, eighth rest; beat 3 is E[-flat]/e[-flat] eighth notes, eighth rest; beat 4 is D/d and C/c eighth notes in *A'* through *D*. M. 233, staff 3, beat 1 is D/d quarter notes; beat 2 is C/c quarter notes in *A'* through *D*. M. 234, beat 2 thru m. 239, beat 3, staff-3 part is doubled an octave higher in *A'* through *D*. M. 245, staff 2, chord 1, cautionary natural is on g' instead of f' in all editions—an error.

CRITICAL NOTES

Mm. 1–2, the contrast of articulation shown by accents in staff 1 (ergo, staff 2) and the slur in staff 3 (both added in edition *E*) should be maintained throughout the main theme—concerning this articulation, Widor suggested, "Listen to the trombones sound the chorale in the overture to *Tannhäuser* and proceed thusly."* Mm. 5 and 6, staves 1 and 2, lower voice, the notation here (especially beat 4, rewritten for *E*) corresponds to the sharper articulation effected by the accents and slur of mm. 1–2.

M. 13, staff 2, chord 1, natural on d' in all editions—an error. M. 44, staff 3, the V-shaped accent marks are unique in Widor's organ symphonies and probably indicate that he was thinking orchestrally—in his revision of Berlioz's *Grand traité* Widor associates these marks specifically with trombones, defining them as signs to take a breath at each note (cf. note to mm. 1–2).† Mm. 58, 59, 62, and 63 have no slurs in any edition—edition follows *Emend* 2. M. 80, staff 3, registration directive "**Péd.** (Fonds) solo" appears in all editions—when the staff-3 part was transferred to staff 2 in *E*, "solo" should have been deleted since manual-to-pedal couplers are indicated at m. 83, beat 4; the edition indicates the change of Pédale registration at m. 56, where manual registrations are changed. M. 83, staff 2, beat 4, crescendo hairpin is located above staff 3 in all editions.

M. 109, staff 1, beat 1 is quarter notes, and beat 2 has no manual directive (it remains **GPR**) in any edition—edition follows *Emend* 2; in a letter dated 21 November 1933, an English organist, Allan Biggs, writing to thank Widor for enlightening him on several passages in this movement, specifically mentions the change of manuals from **G[PR]** to **PR** in this passage. M. 113, staff 1, beat 2 has no manual directive (it remains **GPR**) in any edition—edition follows *Emend* 2. M. 117, staff 1 has no manual directive (it remains **GPR**) in any edition—edition follows *Emend* 2. M. 121, staff 1, beat 1, Widor wrote "G" (shorthand for **GPR**) and then crossed it out in *Emend* 2. M. 122, staff 1, beat 1, Widor wrote "PR" in *Emend* 2—since the return to **G[PR]** is crossed out in m. 121, the directive is not needed. M. 123, staff 1, beat 1 has no manual directive (it remains **GPR** from m. 98) in any edition—edition follows *Emend* 2. M. 124, staff 2 has half rest, quarter rest, eighth rest in all editions—this accounts for less than a full measure. M. 136, staff 1, slur ends on the second half of beat 2 in *B/B'*, *C'/D*, and *E*—this is likely an engraver's error made when the slurring was revised for *B*.

M. 152, the question of pedal couplers is not clear—Widor gives only the *p* dynamic mark, but **Péd** solo probably yields the greatest clarity. M. 162, staff 1, chord 1, d' has no sharp—edition follows *Emend* 2. M. 163, staff 1, a registration directive reads, "**P** Fonds de 4 et de 8" in all editions—edition indicates making the change for **P** at m. 151. M. 167, staff 1, beat 4, manual directive is **P** in all editions—it should have been corrected to **PR** in *E*, being the continuation of **PR** in m. 164. M. 172, staff 2, upper voice, note 6 has no sharp—edition follows *Emend* 2. M. 173, staff 1, beat 2, note 2 has **PR** in all editions—this directive (needed in *A'*, *B/B'* and *C'/D*) should have been deleted in *E* (**R** and **P** are coupled from m. 164). M. 175, staff 2, note 2, a registration directive reads, "**G** Fonds 4, 8, 16" in all editions—edition indicates making the change for **G** at m. 151. Mm. 189, 192, and 193, staff 1, dyad 2 is quarter notes in all editions—the eighth notes, eighth rest of this edition conform to the notation established in mm. 186–88, 190–91, and 194; here the simultaneous change of manual necessitates a break between dyads 2 and 3; Widor, knowing this, certainly did not intend that the performer try to hold dyad 2 a full quarter value, but his original notation also clearly discourages cutting short the established eighth-note duration because of a manual change. M. 192, beat 1, a registration directive reads, "(anches du Récit, *pp*)" in all editions—this directive should have been deleted in *E* when the change of registration for the Récit was deleted from m. 163 (see critical report for *A'-D*). M. 199, staff 2, note 2, the editor questions the flat here—see corresponding report for *A'-D*.

M. 225, staff 3, note 2, "m.g." [main gauche] is written in *Emend* 2, suggesting that the pedal part might be omitted—Widor certainly wrote this thinking of organists of lesser ability; the composer himself, once described as an "acrobat on the pedals," was not troubled by such passages.‡ Mm. 226–27, staves 1 and 2 have no slurs in any edition—edition follows *Emend* 2 (notice that the slurs differ somewhat from those in mm. 58–59). M. 245, staff 2, chord 1, cautionary natural is on g' instead of f' in all editions—an error. M. 246, although it is Widor's general practice (and that of this edition) to place grace notes after the barline—even when they are full "grace chords" as in Symphonie V, V.Toccata, final measure—this grace chord appears correctly placed *before* the barline since it corresponds to the usual anacrusis dominant-and-tonic resolutions in the theme (see mm. 15 and 31).

---

*Charles-Marie Widor, preface to *Jean-Sébastien Bach: Oeuvres complètes pour orgue*, 1 (New York: G. Schirmer, 1914), xix.
†Widor, *The Technique of the Modern Orchestra*, 81.

‡Paul Locard, "Les Maîtres contemporains de l'orgue," *Le Courrier musical* 4 (15 June 1901): 134.

II

Shortly before the composition of this symphony, Widor was among the very first Frenchmen to hear Wagner's *Der Ring des Nibelungen* when he attended the August 1876 premiere in Bayreuth. Not many late-nineteenth-century composers escaped the imprint of Wagner's musical language; that Widor assimilated his share is especially evident in this elegiac slow movement. The expressive fervor of the music derives in part from its sensuous chromaticism and quasi-vocal melodic lines. Widor's acute sensitivity to rhythmic declamation makes the movement sound as though a deeply felt text were being set. The piece is cast in ternary form but with the motivic and rhythmic continuity one expects of the composer; even the connective transitions are motivically cohesive. Because the music seems to demand more expressive subtlety than can be attained from the placid stringlike timbres of an organ, the musical conception really transcends the instrument.

The few cosmetic revisions made to the movement occur mostly in edition *B*; in edition *A'* there is no metronome mark; mm. 34–39, staff 1 has no slurs; m. 47 has *a tempo* instead of Animato; m. 54, staff 1, upper-voice a'[-flat] has no tie into m. 55 (added in *C'*); mm. 73 and 75 have no *rit.* or Tempo I. Edition *E* is the principal source.

The registration scheme is purposefully general until measure 67: measures 1–46 are specified as "Gambes et voix célestes," and measures 47–66 as "Fonds 4, 8, 16." Logic dictates that the Pédale be "Basses 8, 16" (as specified in m. 70) from the beginning—Widor was especially careful to specify when he wanted a pedal line without 16' pitch. While these directions seem to suffice, the lack of coupler indications, as in other movements, raises questions. Widor's intentions here are not as definitively apparent as they are elsewhere; consequently, the editor has let the source's indications stand, with editorial suggestions bracketed in the usual manner. These suggestions stem from the editor's observation that Widor used terraced dynamics quite consistently, thus: **GPR**, **PR**, **R**. The registration directives and the music itself also seem to suggest this.

The intent in measures 1–46 is to emulate the full strings of the orchestra, and so requires the 8' string tones of each manual to be coupled together, as indicated in measure 18—hence, the opening editorial **GPR**. The source's **G** in measure 18 must be interpreted as an abbreviation for at least **GR** (to effect the crescendo and decrescendo in measures 20 and 30 respectively) but more likely for **GPR** (to include the celestes of both **R** and **P**). The use of manual-to-pedal couplers also seems obligatory from the very nature of the writing, the pedal line being an integral part of the manual texture. As usual, the organist must decide which pedal couplers are to be retired when Widor introduces a dynamic mark, such as the *pp* at measure 31—**Péd.** solo is probably appropriate and would have been easily effected at Saint-Sulpice by simply releasing the Grand-choeur-to-Pédale coupler. Whether or not **P** at measure 34, staff 2, is an abbreviation for **PR** may be open to discussion; certainly, if **P** does not include a celeste stop, the coupler is appropriate. The change to "Fonds 4, 8, 16" at measure 47 should be for all three manuals, with all couplers remaining engaged—still assuming terraced dynamics to be the desired effect. Again, the dynamic marks for staff 3 (in mm. 61, 63, and 68) indicate retiring pedal couplers and Fonds (notice that in mm. 70–74, staff 3 is doubled by the lower voice of staff 2 because of the absence of manual-to-pedal couplers). The organist must exercise good judgement and consider the instrument at hand in working out details of registration and use of couplers.

CRITICAL NOTES

M. 25, staff 2, beat 3, rest is sixteenth rest in all editions. M. 38, staff 1, beat 3, a"-flat/c"'-flat dyad has sixteenth flags in all editions—an error; edition follows *Emend* 2. M. 74, staff 1, the thirty-second notes are beamed with those of staff 2 in all editions—this beaming may cause confusion as to whether or not the two notes before the slur, or even all three notes, should be played as part of the arpeggio on the Récit, despite the staff-1 directive* (the three-note figuration is a melodic embellishment—not unusual in Widor's works—and here it takes the place of the anacrusis note of the main melody); staff 2, beat 3, d'[-natural]/f' dyad has sixteenth flags in all editions—an error. M. 90, beat 3, through m. 91 constitute a retransition to the main theme and correspond to m. 16, beat 3, through m. 17, both passages being marked *più lento*—the latter passage, however, is followed by further transitional material marked *a tempo*, so that the return of the main theme in m. 21 is also played *a tempo*; it is possible that the return of the main theme in m. 92 should also be played *a tempo*.

III. Intermezzo

The Intermezzo exhibits extraordinary *éclat* with its figurations punched out of the fiery choruses of reeds and cornets. It is in ternary form: the A sections are dominated by a staccato broken-chord texture and concluded with codettas (at mm. 87 and 259 respectively); the B section (mm. 99–172) provides contrast with its conjunct, legato melodies in imitative (sometimes strictly canonic) three-part texture.

There are five versions of this movement: *A'*, *B*, *B'*, *C'/D*, and *E*. Not atypically for Widor, these multiple versions resulted, in part, from his repeated revisions of the same passages, and this offers an excellent opportunity to observe the creative process. Variant readings in editions *A'* and *B* and in version *C'/D* are given as Appendixes 2 through 4. For the final version, edition *E* is the principal source. Instructions for performing versions *A'*, *B*, *B'*, and *C'/D* complete are given with the respective critical reports for the appendixes. A few apparently unintentional irregularities in the staccato

---

*That the three notes are to be played on **G** Flûte 8' is specifically marked in *Riem* 6.

markings between the two parallel A sections have been tacitly regularized.

As in other movements in this symphony, the question of couplers needs to be resolved. The source gives the registration as "**GPR.** Anches et cornets de 4 et de 8.—**Péd.** Fonds 8, 16 accouplés aux Claviers." While the registration directive explicitly specifies the manual-to-pedal couplers, the intermanual couplers are mandated by the grouping of **GPR** and, implicitly, by the need to counterbalance the bass. The style of writing, too, suggests the usual scheme of terraced dynamics: **GPR**, **PR**, **R**. Widor's use of single manual directives throughout the movement is another indisputable example of his tendency to abbreviate the full directives when the intent seems clear. This edition indicates **GPR** in lieu of the source's **G**, and **PR** in lieu of **P**. (An alternative on some organs might be: **GR**, **PR**, **R**.) Notice that the swell box is required to effect the *mf* in measure 16 and the return to *f* in measure 24 (and analogous mm. 188 and 196). **R** to Pédale may best remain engaged at measure 99 (*pp*) in order to maintain parity with the imitative manual parts. The "**G** Anches" directive at the beginning of the second A section (m. 172) indicates engaging the Grand-orgue pédale de combinaison on top of the Fonds 8' and 4' (specified in the B section); from this it may be concluded that the initial registration should also include manual Fonds 8' and 4' in addition to the specified Anches and Cornets.

CRITICAL NOTES

M. 70, staff 1, beat 1 begins with beamed figuration d'/g' dyad, b[-flat] staccato sixteenth notes—edition follows *Emend* 2. M. 86, staff 3, extension of the slur follows analogous slurring in second A section (mm. 258–59). M. 157, staff 2, note 2, a registration directive in all editions reads, "**G** (Fonds 4, 8.) accouplé au Récit" —edition suggests preparing this at m. 100, where the left hand is free. M. 242, staff 1, beat 1 begins with beamed figuration d'/g' dyad, b[-flat] staccato sixteenth notes—edition follows revision of analogous m. 70 in *Emend* 2. M. 260, staff 1, lower voice, notes 1 and 2 are d'', e''[-flat] in *E*, which does not correspond to analogous m. 88—this is certainly an error, made when the passage was reengraved for *E* (the notes of both mm. 88 and 260 in *C'/D* correspond to those of m. 88 in *E*). M. 270, staff 1, upper voice, note 3, the editorial cautionary natural is undoubtedly correct—although contrasting with the b'-flat of m. 98—as it is indicated in red pencil (perhaps in Widor's hand) in *Riem* 6. M. 272, staff 2, chord 2 has eighth flag—an error; the flag was introduced in edition *C'*, but without the concomitant deletion of the slurs or addition of dots and sixteenth rest; the flag is deleted in *Riem* 6.

IV

Widor's melodic gift is well represented by the main theme that weaves through the movement. Of Berliozian length, this theme, heard only twice complete, defines the two-part form of the movement. The first section has one of the composer's typically well-wrought accompaniments. Written in strict three-part counterpoint—the lower voice being in the Pédale—it is in itself an object of beauty, supplying a sort of countermelody to the main theme. After a brief transition, in which the accompaniment transforms into cascades of sextuplets, the theme returns along with essentially the same bass line that accompanies its first statement. The restful coda brings back a last reminiscence of the theme. With the exception of a few cosmetic details, described in the critical notes below, all editions are identical; edition *E* is the principal source.

In *Schw* 6a, measure 4 is bracketed with the comment, "Widor selbst ließ diesen Takt aus!" (Widor himself leaves out this measure). In addition, *Schw* 6b and *Riem* 6 carry identical additional manual directives for measures 54–56, staff 1, as follows: M. 54, note 10 has **P**; m. 55, note 4 has **G**, note 10 has **P**; m. 56, note 4 has **G**. Although these emendations undoubtedly came from the composer, his own emended scores, on which this edition is based, do not include them.

CRITICAL NOTES

There is no metronome mark, and the tempo indication is given as Allegretto in *A'*. Mm. 7 and 8, staff 1, to phrase the melody as in analogous mm. 62–63 and 103–4, break the slur between the last note of m. 7 and the first note of m. 8. M. 10, staff 1, editorial slur follows phrasing in analogous m. 65. Mm. 19 and 20 have no *rit.* and *a tempo* in *A'*. M. 33, staff 1, lower voice, note 1 has no dot in any edition—an error. M. 40, staff 1, lower voice, note 2, editorial quarter note follows m. 38. M. 63, staff 2, note 2 is a[-flat] in all editions—the note is struck through and "mi" is written in the margin of *Emend* 2; the fingering and scale patterns suggest e[-flat] rather than e'[-flat]. Mm. 74 and 75 have no *rit.* and *a tempo* in edition *A'*. Mm. 85 and 93, staff 3, registration directives are added in *C'*. M. 94 has no *più lento* in *A'*.

V. Finale

The drama and intensity of the first movement find equivalency in the scintillating fireworks of the Finale. This movement, a sonata-rondo, is dominated by two main thematic ideas, the first homophonic and rhythmically dynamic (mm. 1–4; note especially the displaced accents in mm. 2 and 4), the second a chain of disjunct appoggiaturas, rhythmically neutral but contrapuntally promising. After the first thematic group (mm. 1–24), transitional passage (mm. 24–48), second thematic group (mm. 48–71), and closing theme (mm. 72–86), the opening idea returns in the tonic key, leading to an extensive development based chiefly on the second of the main thematic ideas (mm. 98–171). The recapitulation (mm. 172 [arguably 176]–230) imaginatively reworks earlier materials before leading to a rousing coda (mm. 230–49).

With the exception of two added tempo directives, all editions are identical. Edition *E* is the principal source.

As in other movements, Widor intended that the dynamics here be terraced. This edition gives **GPR** in lieu of the source's **G**, and **PR** in lieu of **P**. Where it appears unambiguous, editorial staccatos and tenutos are added to conform to Widor's oft repeated policy:

> The uniformity of feet and hands is absolutely necessary, whether you are beginning the note or finishing it. All sounds placed by the composer under the same perpendicular should begin and end together, obeying the *bâton* of the same leader.*

An obvious exception to this rule occurs, of course, when one of the notes in vertical alignment is part of a linearly legato voice (e.g., in mm. 4–5, staff 2, where the lower voice accords with staves 1 and 3, contrasting the legato upper voice). It should also be observed that there are many instances when the note at the end of a slur must be played short, as if with a staccato dot, to correspond to other notes in the same vertical alignment (e.g., m. 11, staff 1, beat 4, upper voice—see also m. 17, staff 1, beat 3, upper voice, where there is no alternative).

Critical Notes

The metronome mark is added in *B*. M. 34, staff 3, note 1 has no staccato dot—it faded from the pressing after *D*. M. 60, *Riem*6 has the following manual directives: staff 1, beat 2 has **P**; staff 2, beat 2 has **R**—this continues the pattern in mm. 56 and 58. M. 122, staff 1, grace note has no accidental in any edition—edition follows *Emend* 2. M. 125, staff 3, note 2, editorial staccato follows m. 121. M. 156, staff 1, upper voice, note 3 is b'[-sharp] in all editions—edition follows *Emend* 2; lower voice, beat 4 is quarter rest in all editions—editorial d' follows pattern in mm. 155, 158, et seq. (the engraver may have mistaken a d' quarter note for a quarter rest). M. 185, staff 2, beat 4 is g'/b' dyad in all editions—edition follows *Emend* 2. M. 220, staff 3, beat 4 is E/e accented quarter notes (no slur) in all editions—edition follows *Emend* 2. M. 221, *allargando molto* is added in *E*; staves 1 and 2, the editorial *sf* marks follow editions *A'* through *D*—they were deleted to make room for the *allargando molto* directive placed between the staves in *E*; staff 3, beat 1 is e/e' accented half notes (no slur) in all editions—edition follows *Emend* 2. M. 229, *rit.* added in *E*.

Appendix 1

I. Edition A', versions B/B' and C'/D, mm. 123–31. This Appendix complements and completes the reports given under "Variants in Editions *A'* through *D*" in the critical notes.

M. 124, staff 2 has half rest, quarter rest, eighth rest—this accounts for less than a full measure.

Appendix 2

III. Intermezzo. Edition A', mm. 81–100, 253–73. To perform this edition complete, play mm. 1–80 of edition

---

*Charles-Marie Widor, "John Sebastian Bach and the Organ," trans. by B. L. O'Donnell, in R. Grey, ed., *Studies in Music* (London: Simpkin, Marshall, Hamilton, Kent, 1901), 61.

E; then mm. 81–100 of this Appendix; then mm. 101–252 of edition *E*, noting the variants reported below; then mm. 253–73 of this Appendix, noting the variants reported below.

Mm. 98–99, staff 1 has slur extending from f sixteenth-note upbeat to m. 99 to m. 99, note 2—the editor believes the engraver mistook a (carelessly written?) autograph tie for a slur; in the present edition the passage conforms to parallel mm. 270–71.

Measures 100–252 in edition *A'* differ from edition *E* as follows. M. 129, staff 1 has e'[-flat] half note tied into the next measure. M. 130, staff 1 has (tied) e'[-flat] half note tied into the next measure. M. 155, staff 1 has e'[-flat] half note tied into the next measure. M. 156, staff 1 has (tied) e'[-flat] half note tied into the next measure.

Measures 253–69 in edition *A'* differ from mm. 81–97 as follows. M. 259, staves 1 and 2 have *ff* on second half of beat 1.

Appendix 3

III. Intermezzo. Edition B, mm. 81–100, 253–73. To perform edition *B* complete, play mm. 1–80 of the present edition; then mm. 81–100 of this Appendix; then mm. 101–252 of the present edition; then mm. 253–73 of this Appendix with the following variants: m. 259, staves 1 and 2 have *ff* on second half of beat 1. Mm. 267–68, staff 2, note 3 (g) is also stemmed up as quarter note and tied into the following measure, where first half of beat 1 is g/g' eighth notes. Mm. 268–69, staff 2, note 3 (g) is also stemmed up as quarter note and tied into the following measure, where first half of beat 1 is g/g' eighth notes.

Mm. 98–99, staff 1 has slur extending from f sixteenth-note upbeat to m. 99 to m. 99, note 2—see parallel report in Appendix 2.

To perform edition *B'* complete, play mm. 1–86 of the present edition with the following variant: m. 85, staff 3, beat 1 is f quarter note; then mm. 87–100 of this Appendix, noting the variants reported below; then mm. 101–258 of the present edition with the following variant: m. 257, staff 3, beat 1 is f quarter note; then mm. 259–73 of this Appendix, noting the variants reported below.

Edition *B'* differs from edition *B* in mm. 81–100 and 253–73 as follows. M. 94, staff 1, beat 2, chord is e"[-flat]/a"[-natural]/e'"[-flat], tied into next measure. M. 95, staff 1, chord 1 is (tied) e"[-flat]/a"[-natural]/e'"[-flat], chord 2 is d"/b"[-natural]/d'". M. 266, staff 1, see report for m. 94. M. 267, staff 1, see report for m. 95.

Appendix 4

III. Intermezzo. Version C'/D, mm. 87–96, 259–68. To perform version *C'/D* complete, play mm. 1–86 of edition *E*, then this Appendix, then mm. 97–258 of edition *E*, then this Appendix, then mm. 269–73 of edition *E*. Edition *D* is the principal source.

M. 267, staff 2, beat 1, note 4 is g'—an error.

Widor's *Avant-propos*

Although it may not be customary to place a preface at the front of musical editions, I believe it is necessary to put one here in order to explain the character, the style, the procedures of registration, and the sign conventions of these eight symphonies.

Old instruments had almost no reed stops: two colors, white and black, foundation stops and mixture stops—that was their entire palette; moreover, each transition between this white and this black was abrupt and rough; the means of graduating the body of sound did not exist. Consequently, Bach and his contemporaries deemed it pointless to indicate registrations for their works—the mixture stops traditionally remaining appropriate to rapid movements, and the foundation stops to pieces of a more solemn pace.

The invention of the "swell box" dates back to just before the end of the eighteenth century. In a work published in 1772, the Dutchman Hess de Gouda expresses the admiration he felt upon hearing Handel, in London, coming to grips with the new device; some time later, in 1780, Abbé Vogler recommends the use of the "box" in the German manufacture of instruments. The idea gained ground, but without great artistic effect—for in spite of the most perspicacious efforts, they did not succeed in going beyond the limits of a thirty-key manual and an insignificant number of registers.

It was necessary to wait until 1839 for the solution to the problem.

The honor for it redounds to French industry and the glory to Mr. A. Cavaillé-Coll. It is he who conceived the diverse wind pressures, the divided windchests, the pedal systems and the combination registers, he who applied for the first time Barker's pneumatic motors, created the family of harmonic stops, reformed and perfected the mechanics to such a point that each pipe—low or high, loud or soft—instantly obeys the touch of the finger, the keys becoming as light as those of a piano—the resistances being suppressed, rendering the combination of [all] the forces of the instrument practical. From this result: the possibility of confining an entire division in a sonorous prison—opened or closed at will—the freedom of mixing timbres, the means of intensifying them or gradually tempering them, the freedom of tempos, the sureness of attacks, the balance of contrasts, and, finally, a whole blossoming of wonderful colors—a rich palette of the most diverse shades: harmonic flutes, gambas, bassoons, English horns, trumpets, celestes, flue stops and reed stops of a quality and variety unknown before.

The modern organ is essentially symphonic. The new instrument requires a new language, an ideal other than scholastic polyphony. It is no longer the Bach of the fugue whom we invoke but the heartrending melodist, the preeminently expressive master of the Preludes, the Magnificat, the B-minor Mass, the cantatas, and the *St. Matthew Passion*.

But this "expressiveness" of the new instrument can only be subjective; it arises from mechanical means and cannot have spontaneity. While the stringed and wind instruments of the orchestra, the piano, and voices reign only by naturalness of accent and unexpectedness of attack, the organ, clothed in its primordial majesty, speaks as a philosopher: alone among all, it can put forth the same volume of sound indefinitely and thus inspire the religious idea of the infinite. Surprises and accents are not natural to it; they are lent to it, they are accents by adoption. It is clear that their use requires tact and discernment. It is also clear to what extent the organ symphony differs from the orchestral symphony. No confusion is to be feared. One will never write indiscriminately for the orchestra or for the organ, but henceforth one will have to exercise the same care with the combination of timbres in an organ composition as in an orchestral work.

Rhythm itself must come under the influence of modern trends: it must lend itself to a sort of elasticity of the measure, all the while preserving its rights. It must allow the musical phrase to punctuate its paragraphs and breathe when necessary, provided that it hold [the phrase] by the bit and that [the phrase] march to its step. Without rhythm, without this constant manifestation of the will returning periodically to the strong beat, the performer will not be listened to. How often the composer hesitates and abstains at the moment of writing on his score the *poco ritenuto* that he has in his thought! He does not dare, from fear that the exaggeration of the performer may weaken or break the flow of the piece. The indication is left out. We do not have the graphic means for emphasizing the end of a period, or reinforcing a chord by a type of pause of unnoticeable duration. Isn't it a great shame, especially since the organ is an instrument that draws all of its effect from time values?

As to terminology, the system indicating the disposition of timbres—usage having established nothing as yet—it seemed practical to me to note the manual and pedal registration at the head of each piece; to apportion by tone colors, rather than an exact nomenclature of stops, the intensity of the sonorities of the same family; to designate the manuals by their abbreviations (two or more initials juxtaposed signifying the coupling of two or more manuals); to assume the reed stops always prepared; and finally to reserve *fff* for the full power of the organ, without having to mention the introduction of the ventil (Anches) pedals. In the combination **GR**

[Grand-orgue, Récit], the crescendo applies only to the Récit, unless this crescendo leads to the *fff*, in which case all the forces of the instrument must enter little by little in order, flues and reeds.

It is unnecessary, I believe, to implore the same precision, the same coordination of the feet and hands in leaving a keyboard as in attacking it, and to protest against all carrying-over of the pedal after the time, an old-fashioned custom that has happily almost disappeared.

With the consummate musicians of today, the insufficiencies and shortcomings in musical notation become less worrisome; the composer is more certain of seeing his intentions understood and his implications perceived. Between him and the performer is a steadfast collaboration, which the growing number of virtuosos will render more intimate and fruitful every day.

Ch. M. W.

Symphonie VI in G Minor

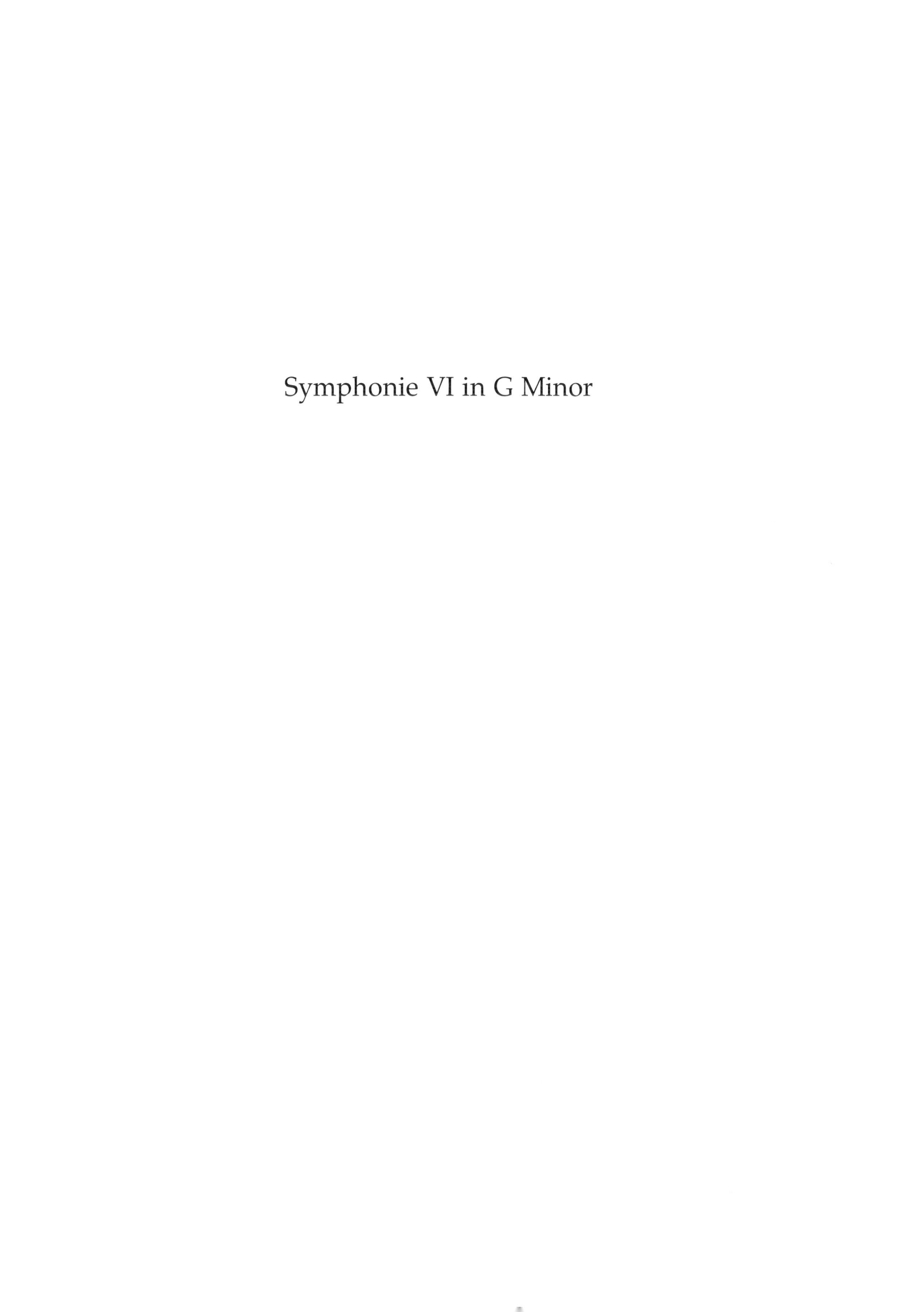

I

quasi recitativo, a piacere ma agitato

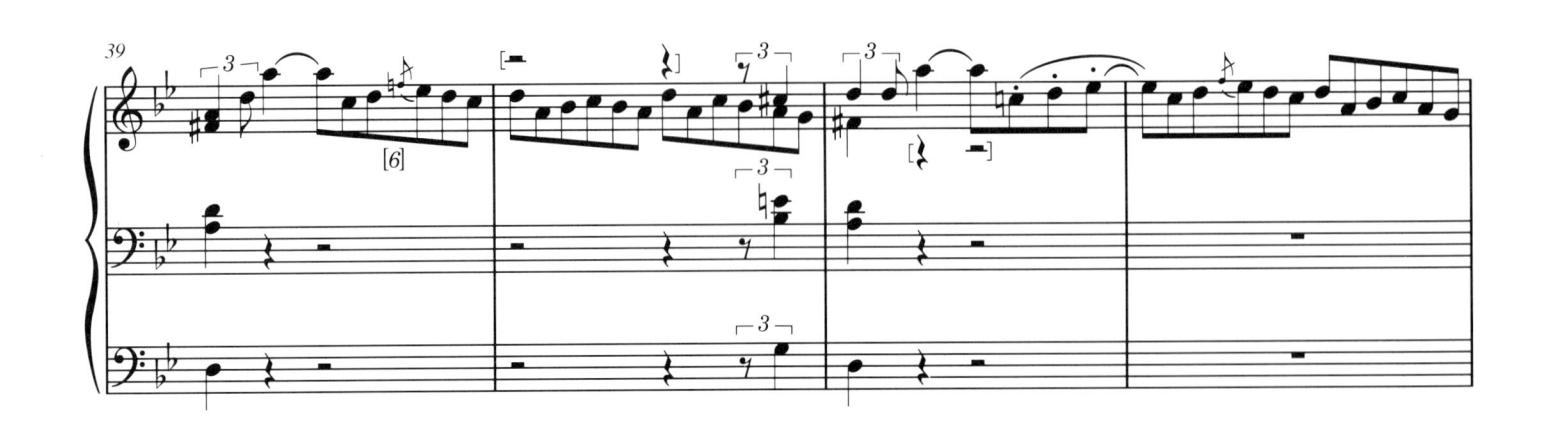

a tempo
rit.
fff
Adagio
R
GPR
p
G Fonds 16', 8', 4'
P Fonds 8', 4'
R [Fonds 16', 8', 4',]Anches 16', 8', 4', pianissimo
(♩ = 132)
staccato
legato il basso
Péd. Fonds [16', 8', 4']

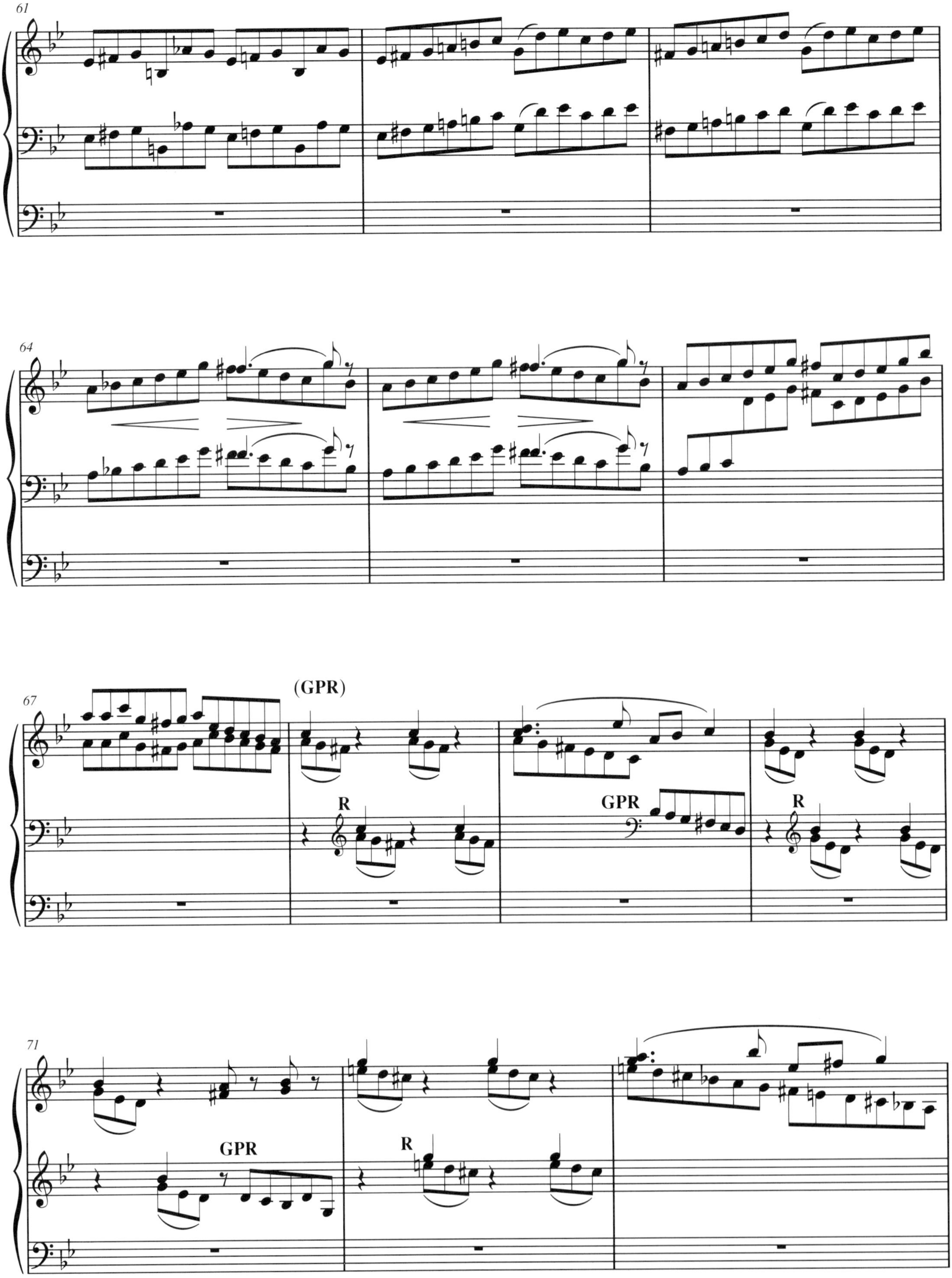
61
64
67
(GPR)
R
GPR
R
71
GPR
R

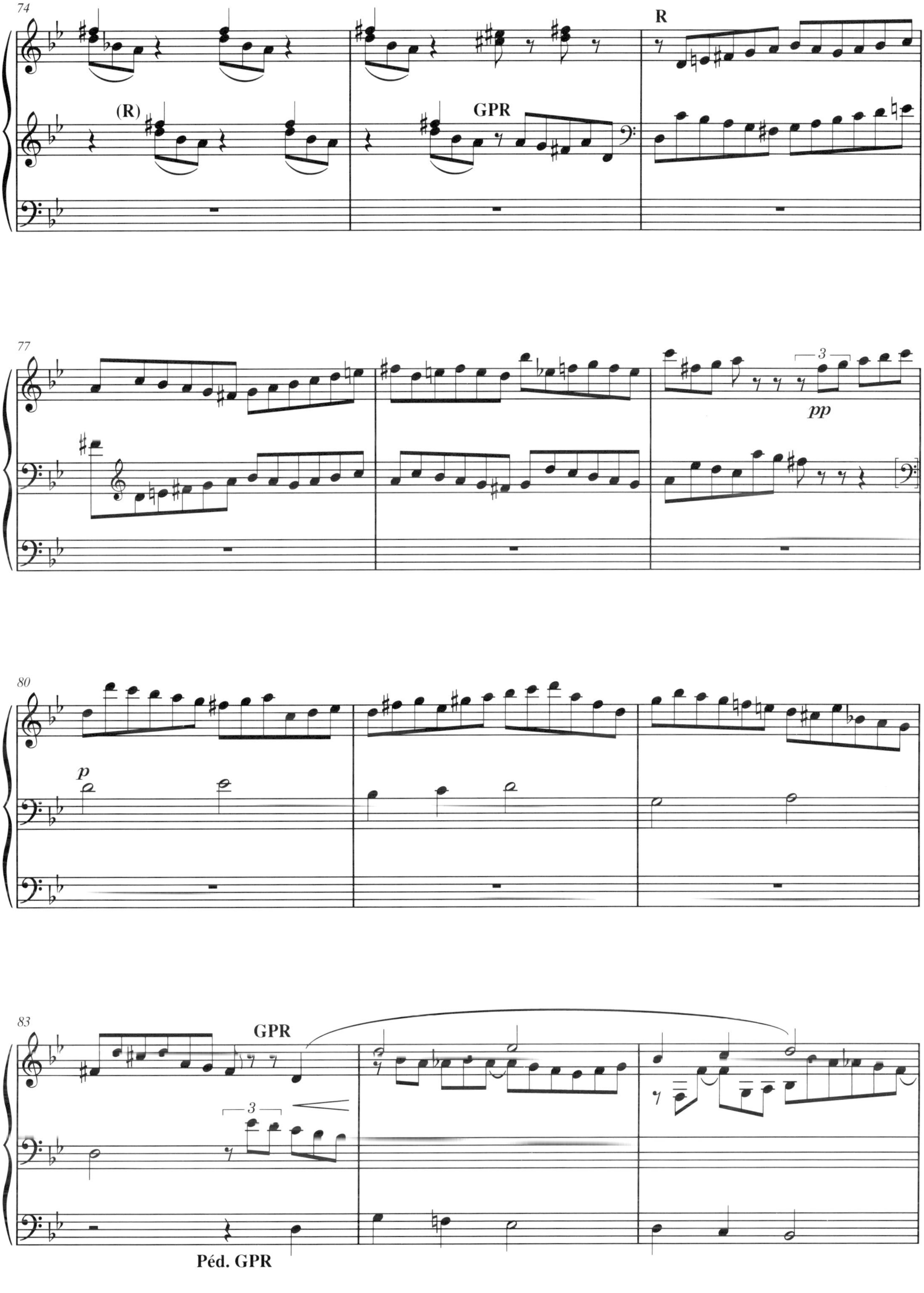
74
R
(R)
GPR
77
pp
80
p
83
GPR
Péd. GPR

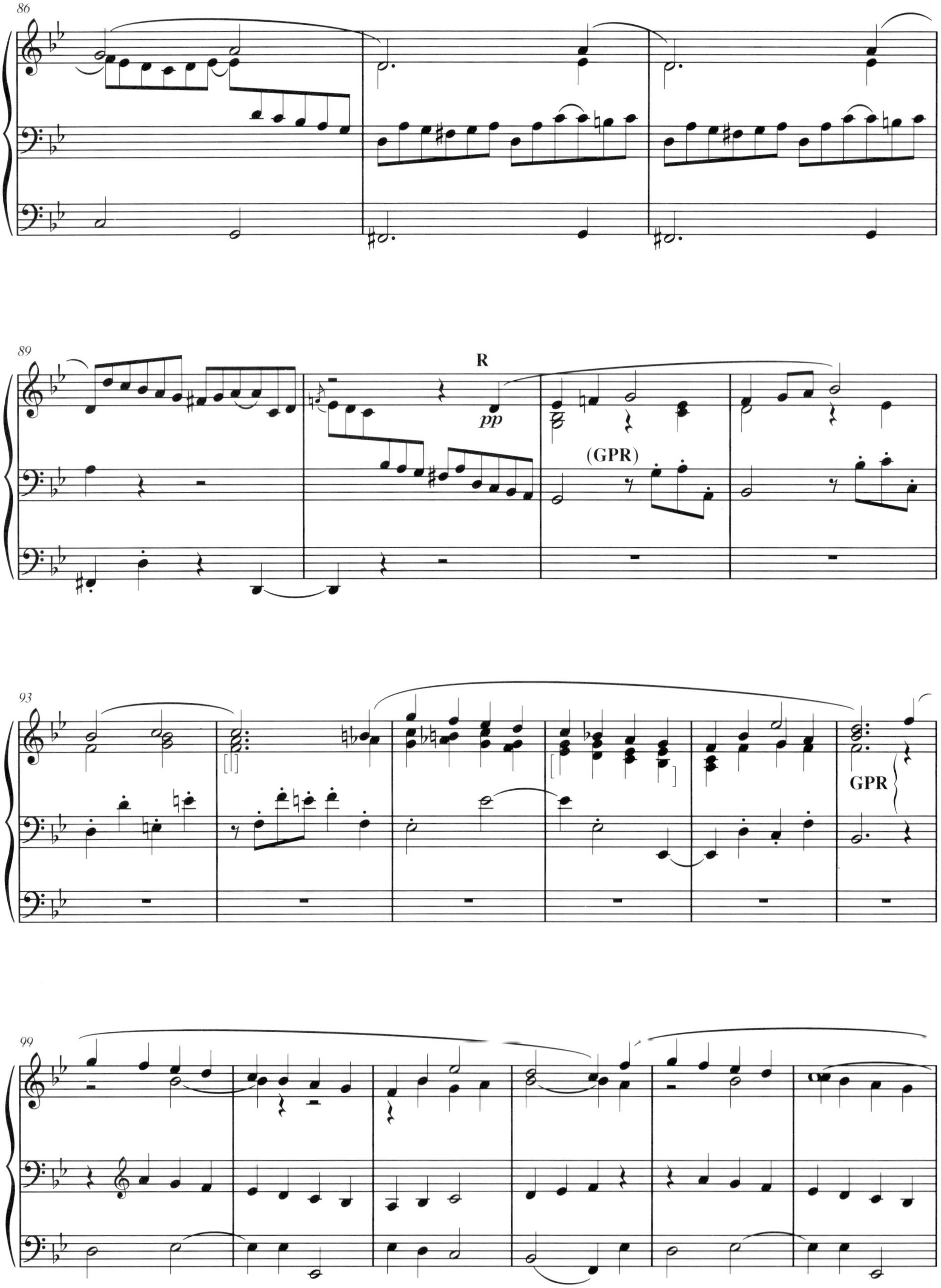
86
89
R
pp
(GPR)
93
GPR
99

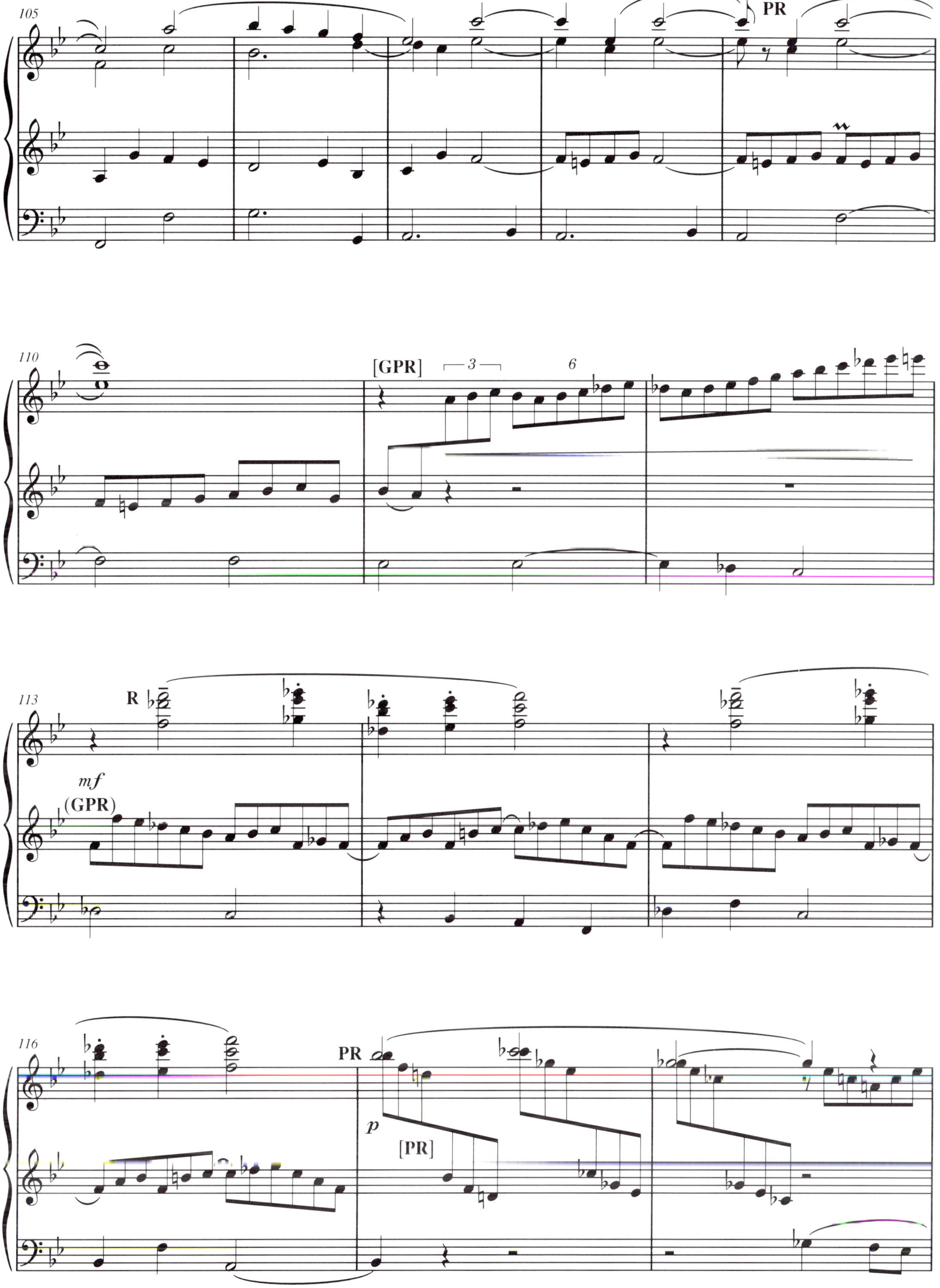
105
PR
110
[GPR]
3
6
113
R
mf
(GPR)
116
PR
p
[PR]

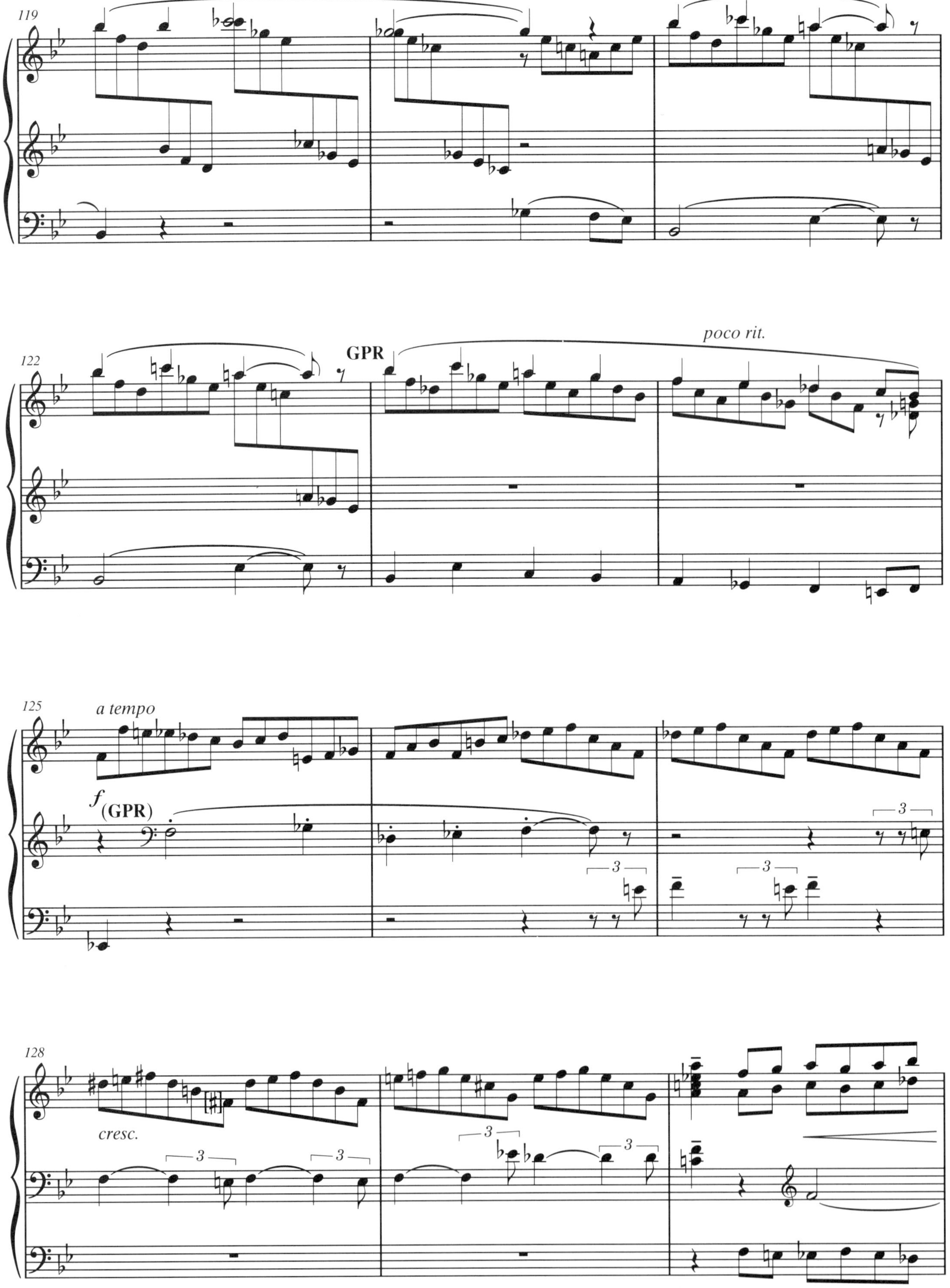
119
122
GPR
poco rit.
125
a tempo
f (GPR)
128
cresc.

Large
131
fff
fff
rit.
136
a tempo
sf
sf
141
largamente
sf
a tempo
R
ff
146
mf
G Fonds 16', 8', 4'
P Fonds 8', 4'
Péd. Fonds 16', 8', 4' [solo]

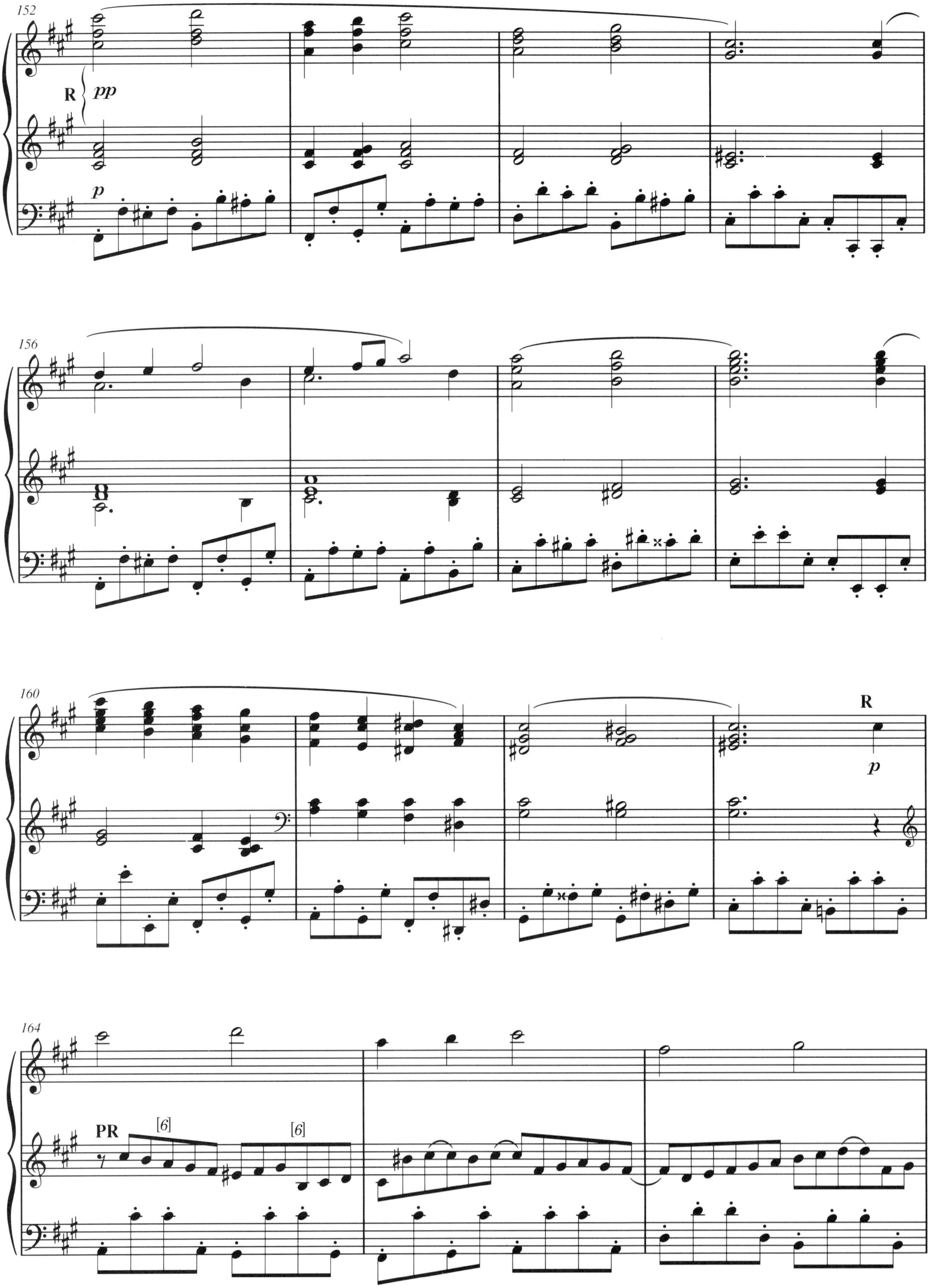
152
R
pp
p
156
160
R
p
164
PR
[6]
[6]

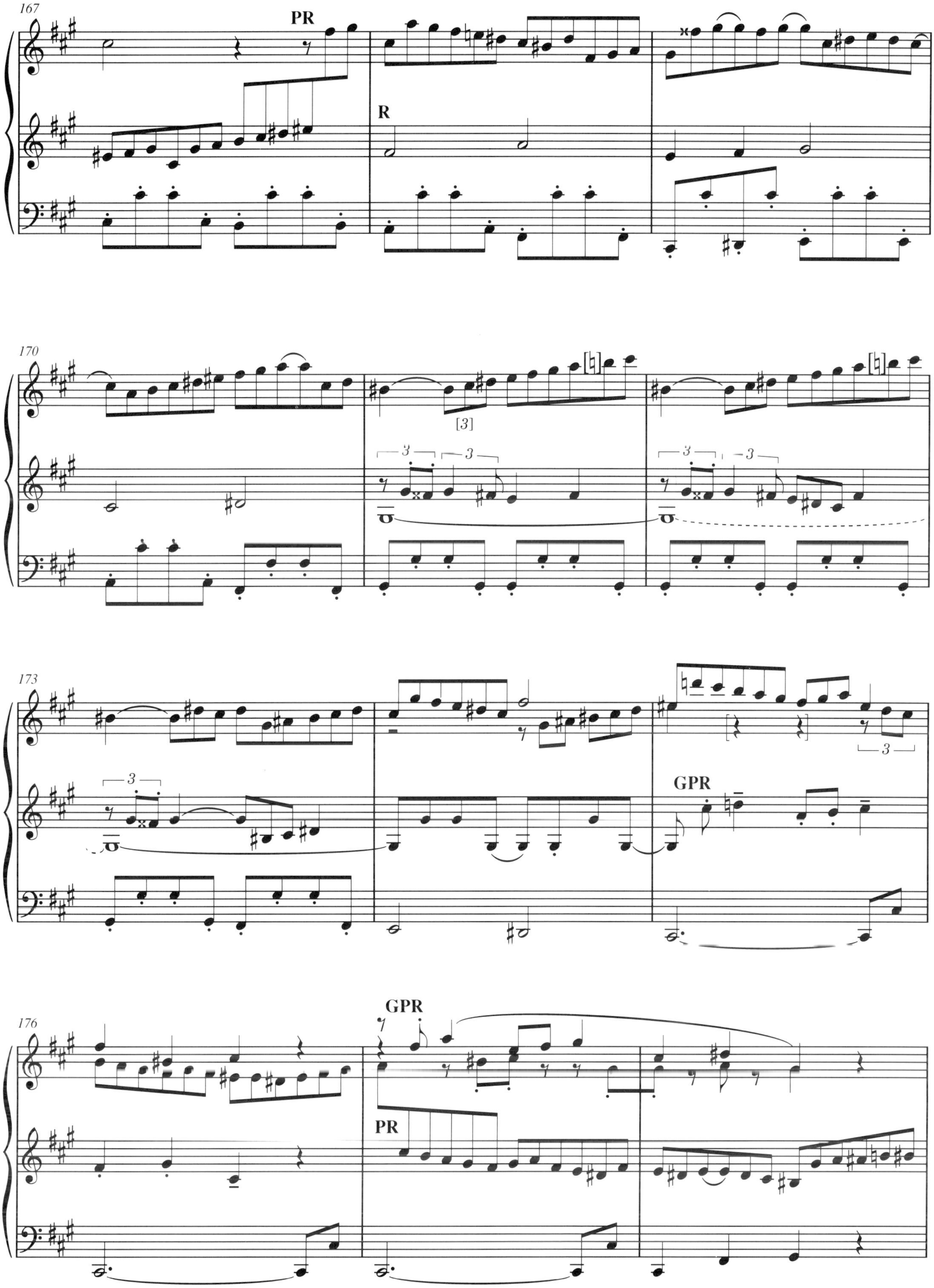
167
PR
R
170
[3]
173
GPR
176
GPR
PR

179
poco rit.
R
a tempo
p
R
182
pp
185
3
GPR
PR
[Péd. GPR]
189
GPR
PR
GPR
GPR
PR
GPR
PR

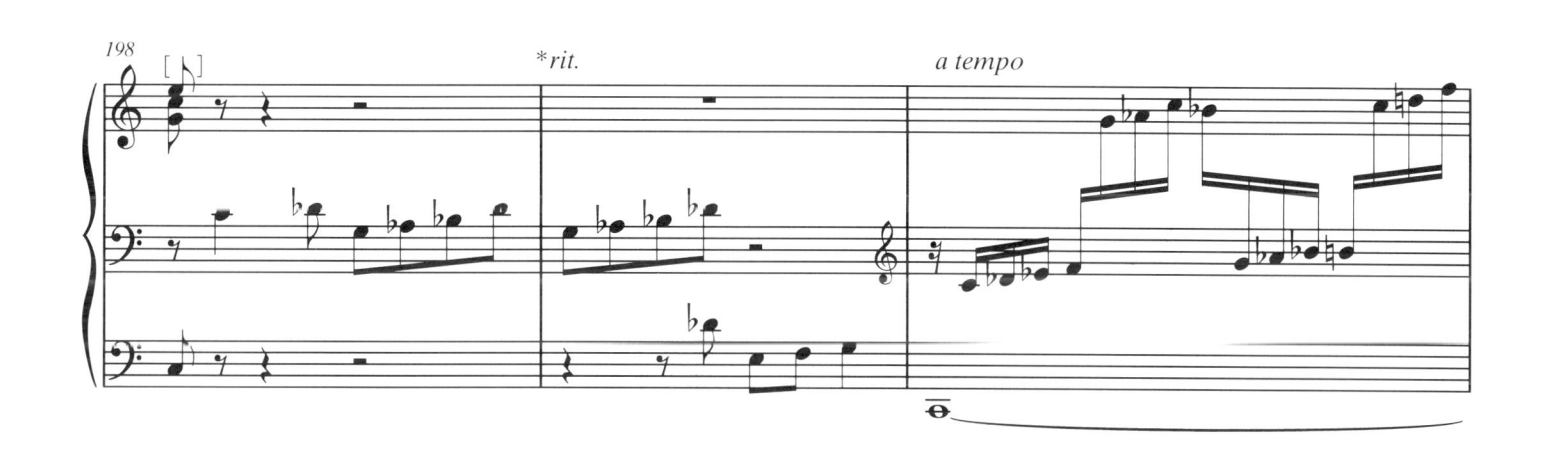

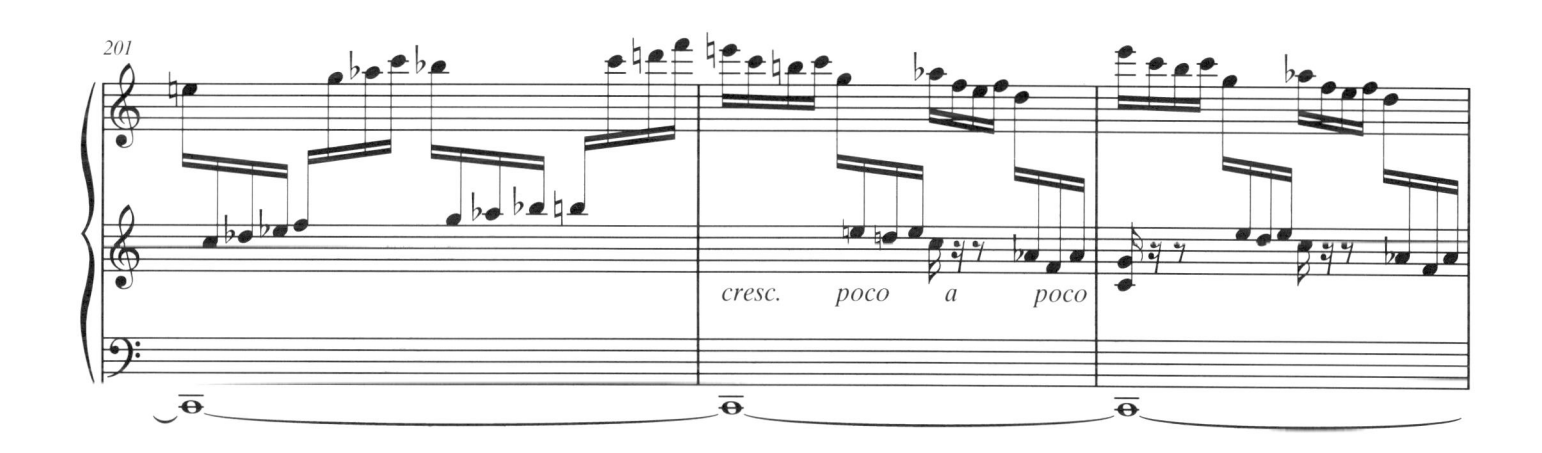

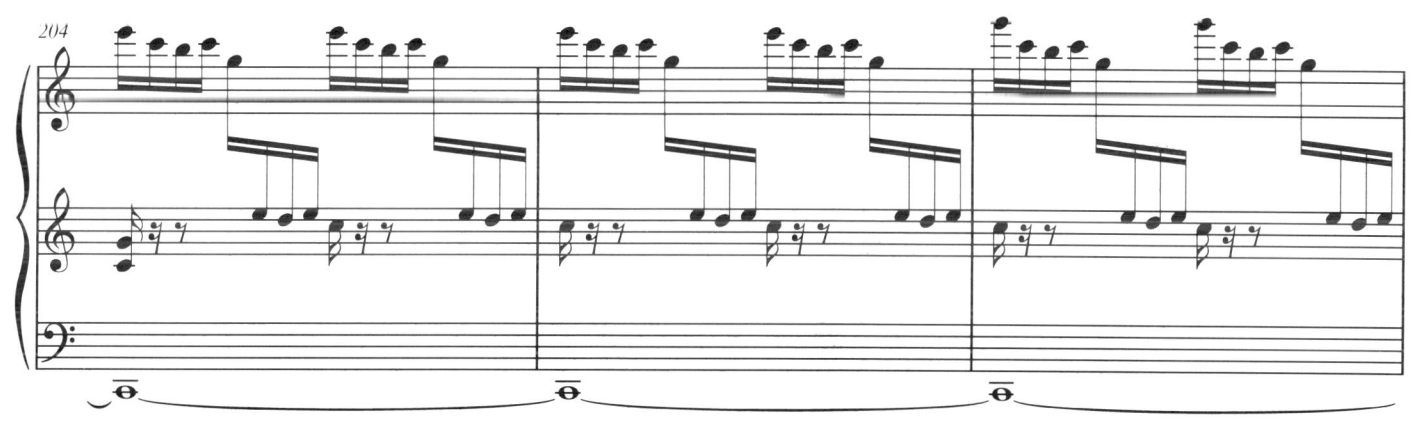

*See Critical Notes.

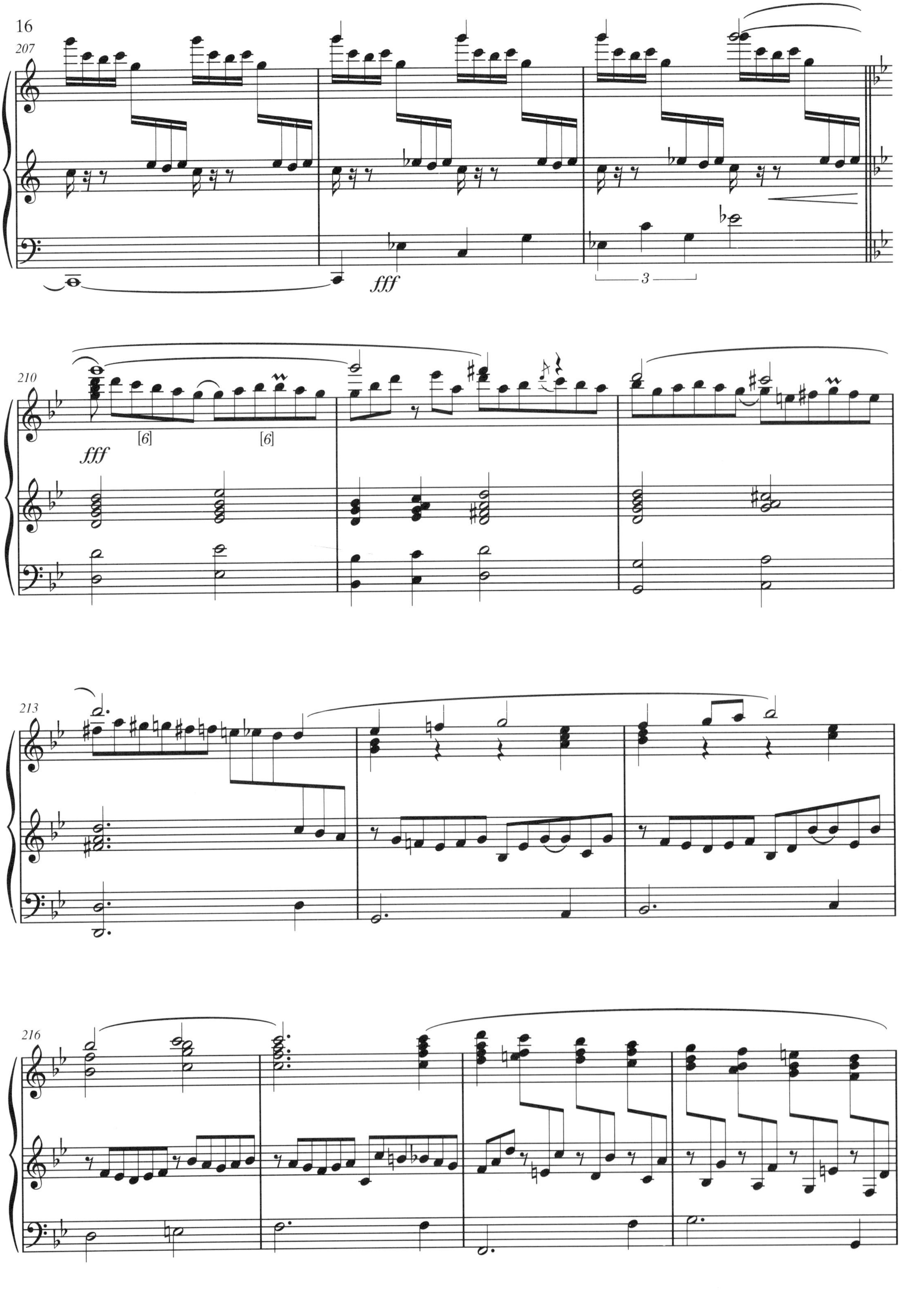
207
fff
3
210
fff
[6]
[6]
213
216

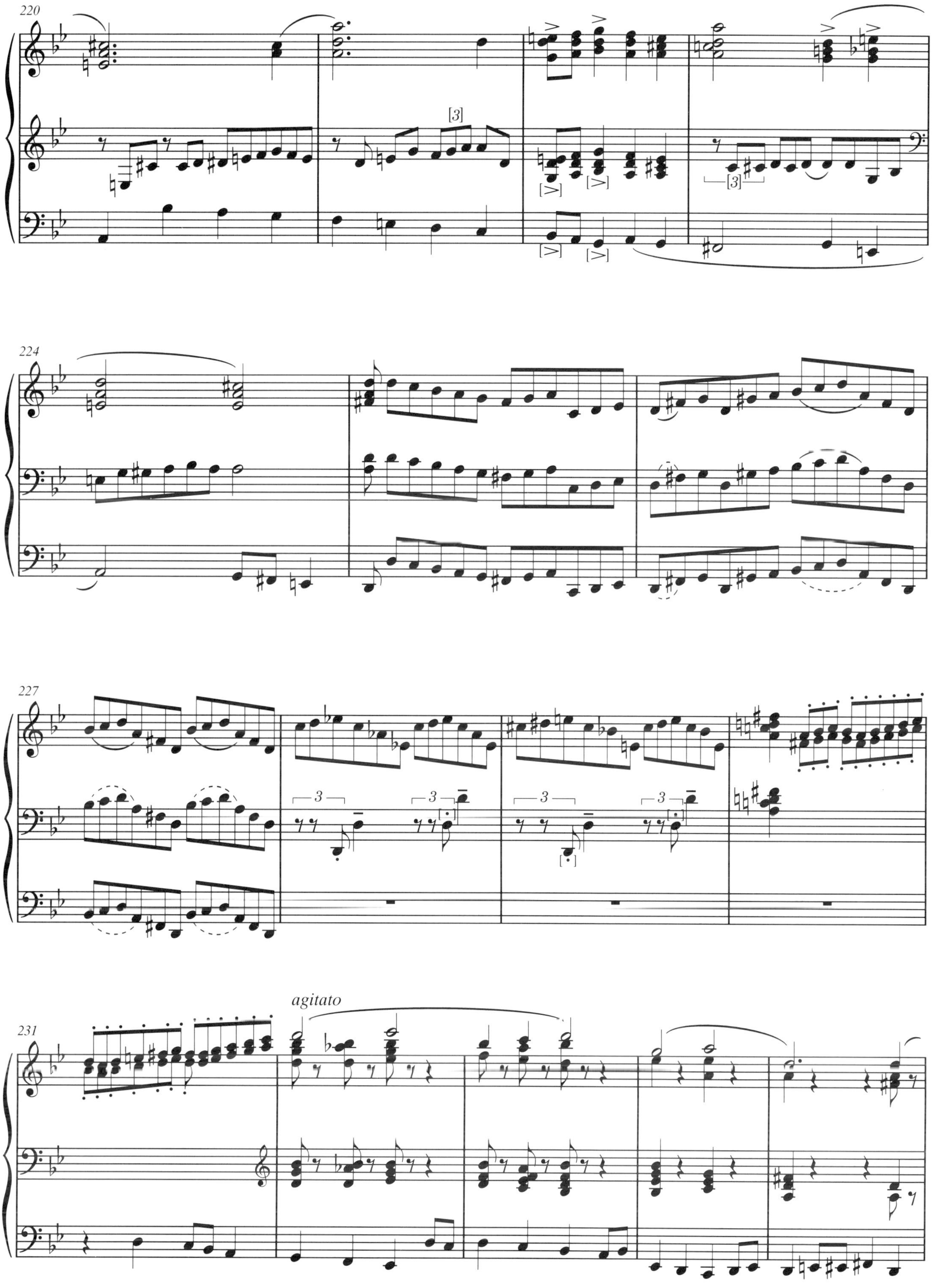
220
[3]
[>]
[>]
[>]
[>]
[3]
224
227
3
3
3
3
231
agitato

18

II

Grand orgue:
Positif: Gambes [8'], Voix célestes
Récit:
Pédale: [Basses 16', 8']

Adagio (♪ = 46)

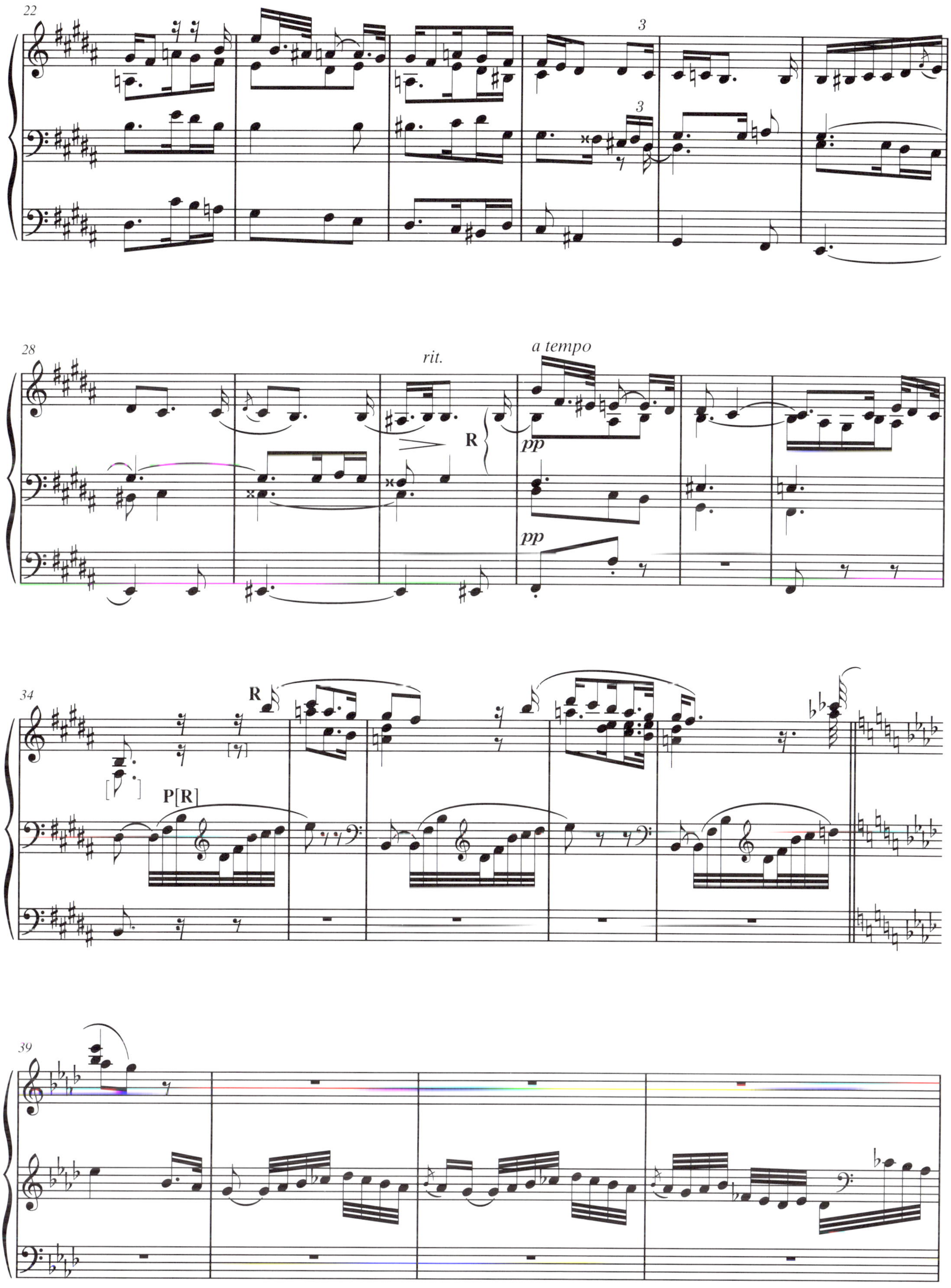
22
3
3
28
rit.
a tempo
R
pp
pp
34
R
P[R]
39

43
[GPR] Fonds 16', 8', 4'
Animato
rit.
G[PR]
ff
ff
Péd. Fonds 32', 16', 8'
[Péd. GPR]
48
53
3
57
P[R]

61
f
mf
P[R]
p
R Flûtes 8', 4'
66
R
pp
p
f
P[R]
Péd. Basses 16', 8'
71
rit.
G Flûte 8' [solo]
Tempo I
R Voix céleste
pp
pp
76

24

Grand orgue: [Fonds 8', 4',]
Positif: Anches 8', 4', Cornets
Récit:
Pédale: Fonds 16', 8'

III. Intermezzo

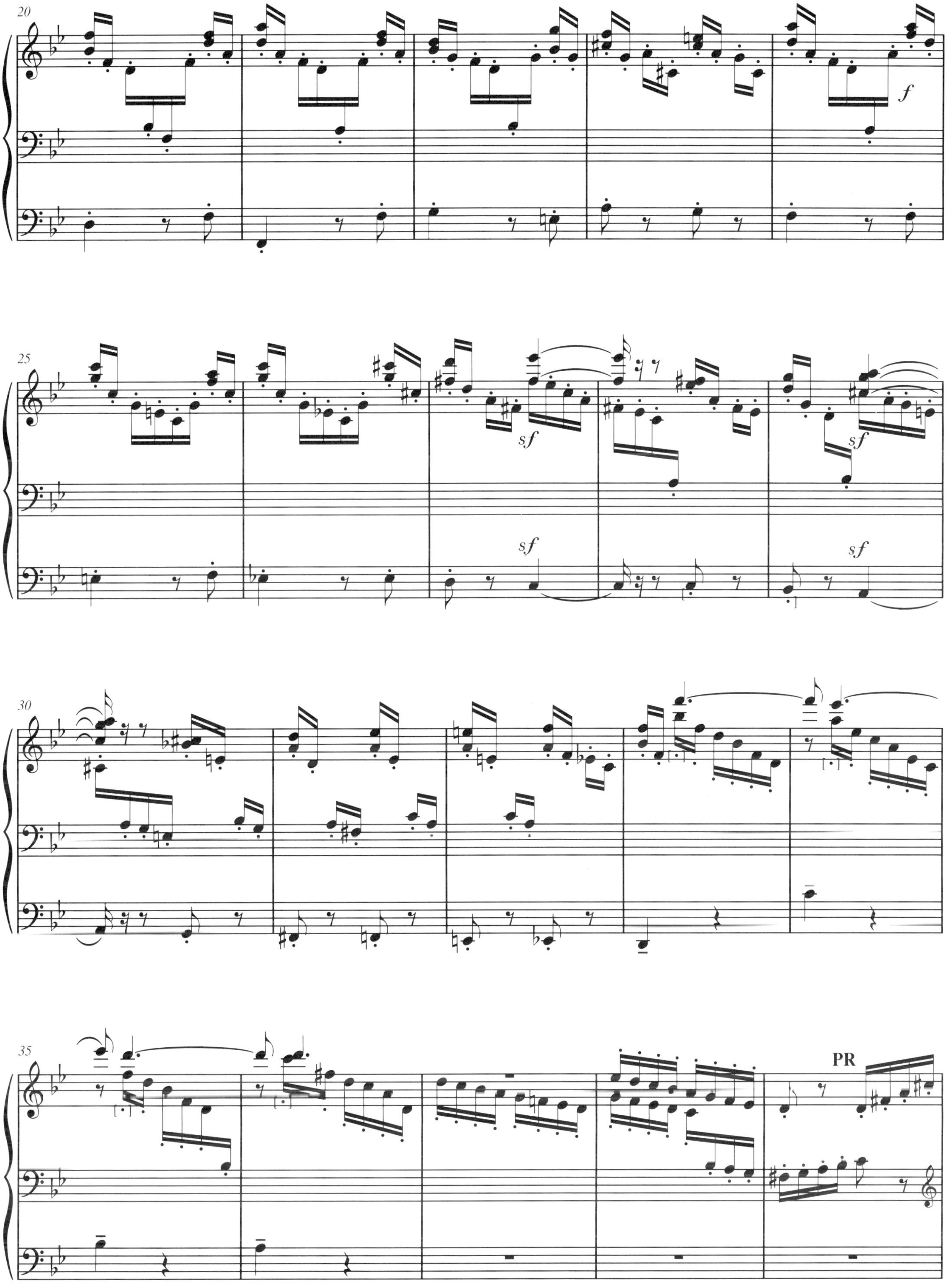
20
f
25
sf
sf
sf
sf
30
35
PR

28

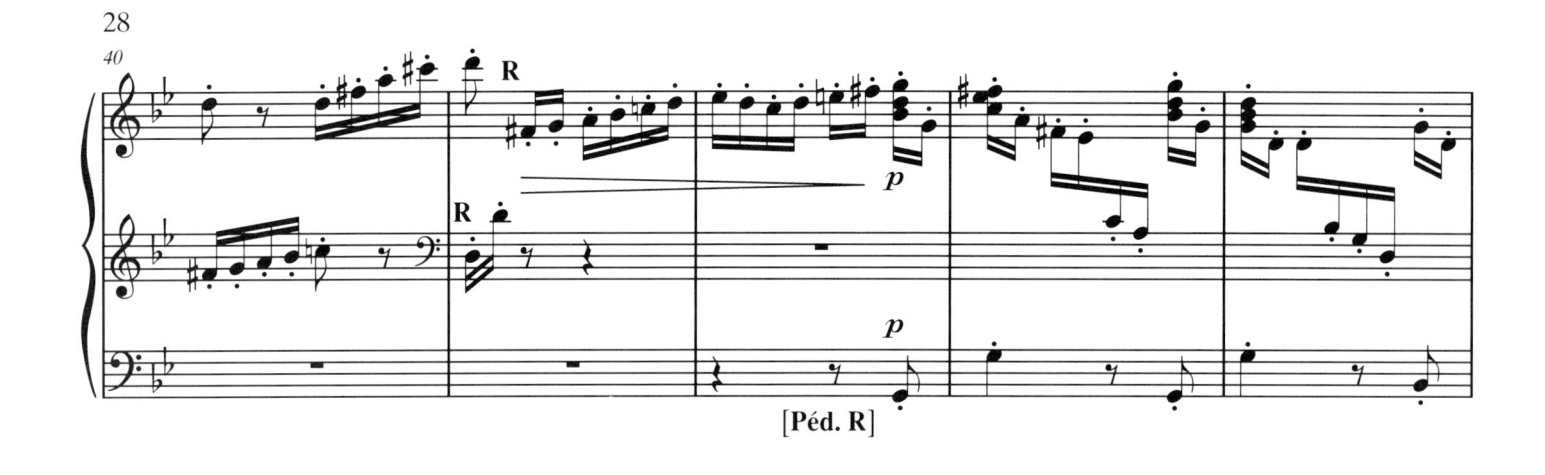

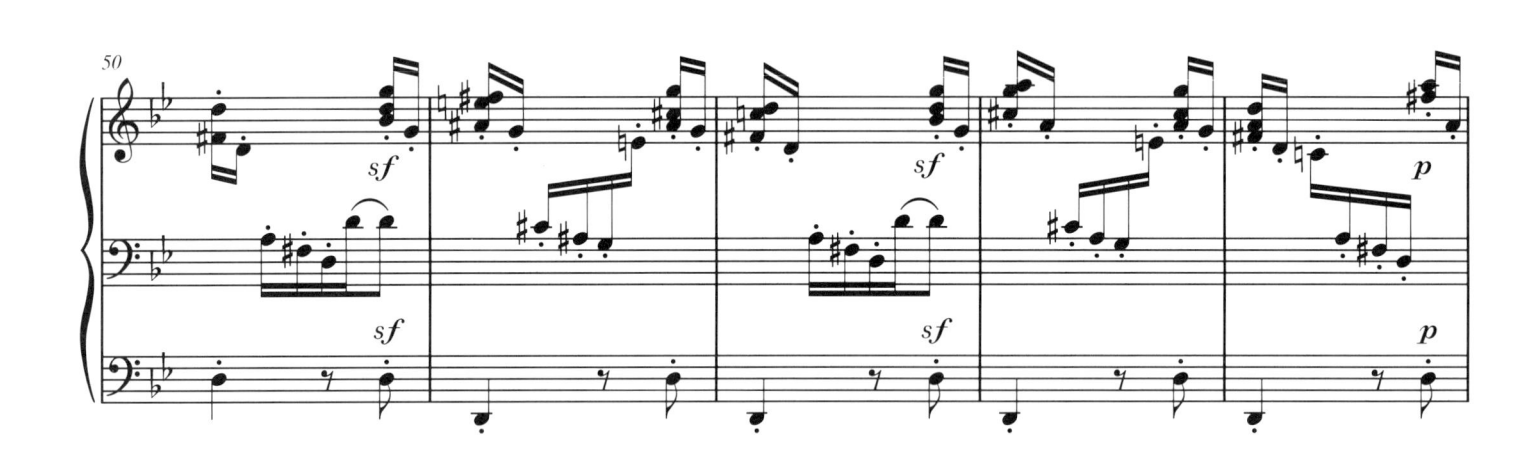

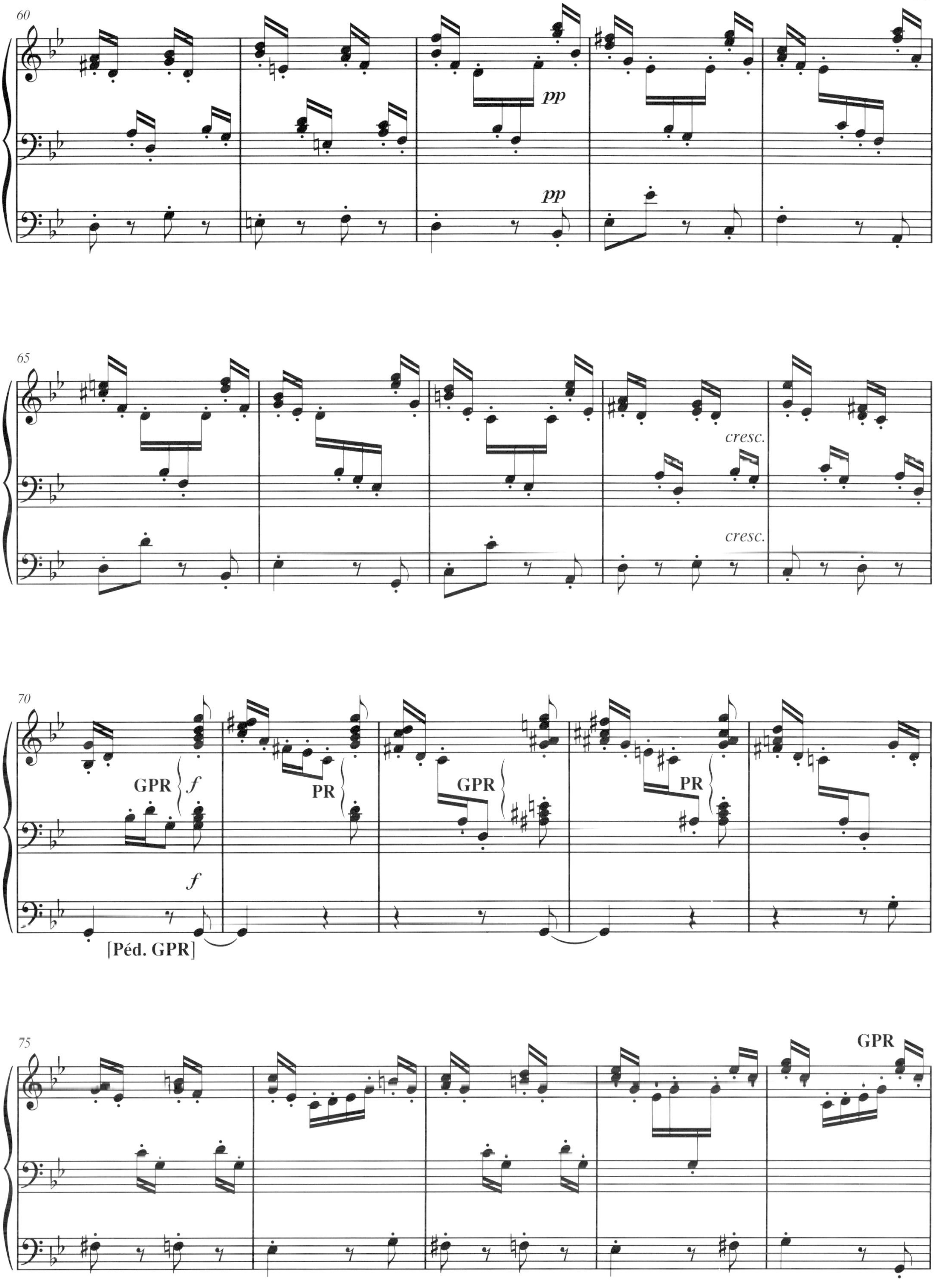
pp
pp
cresc.
cresc.
GPR
f
PR
GPR
PR
f
[Péd. GPR]
GPR

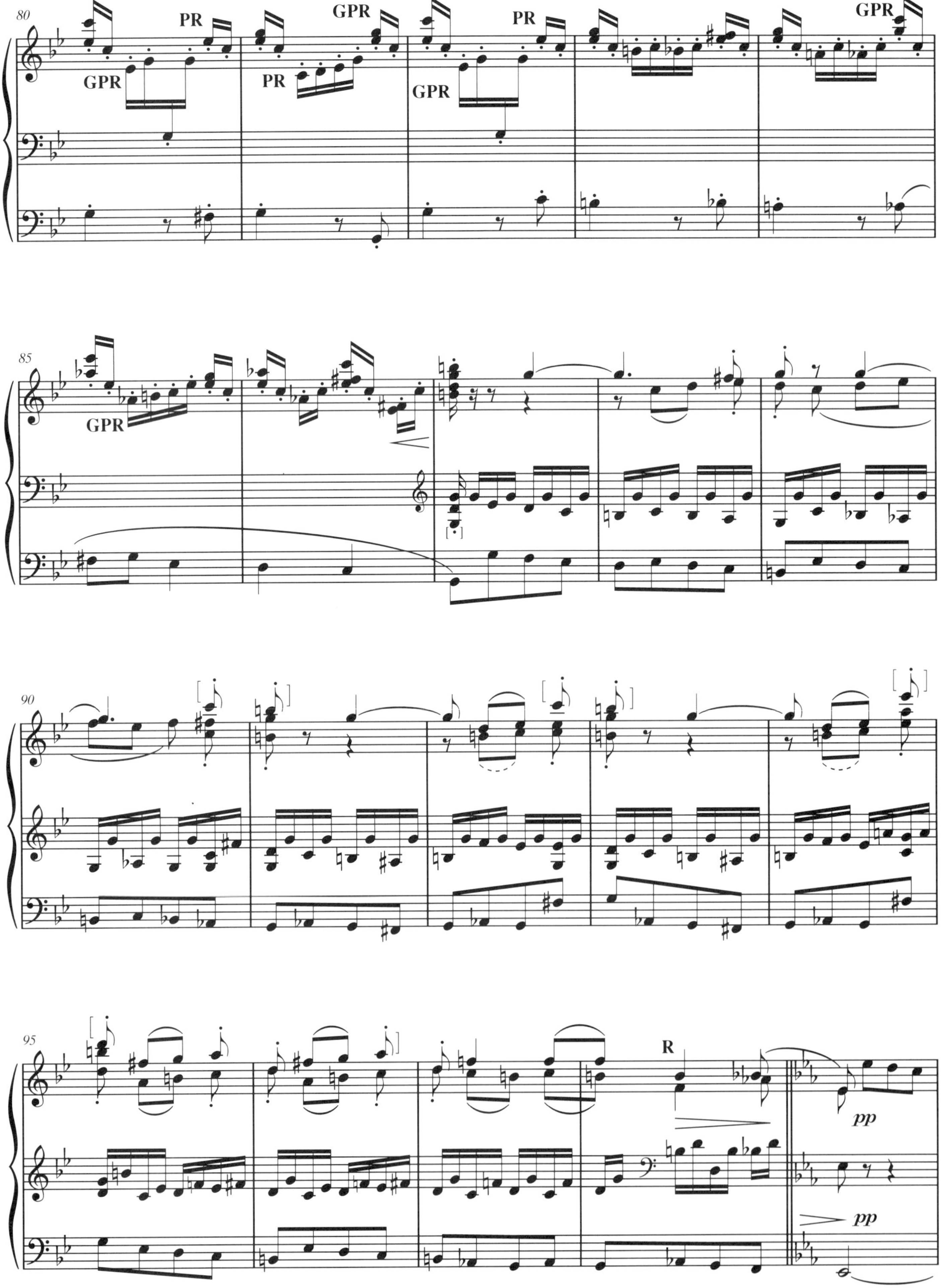
80
PR
GPR
GPR
PR
PR
GPR
GPR
85
GPR
90
95
R
pp
pp

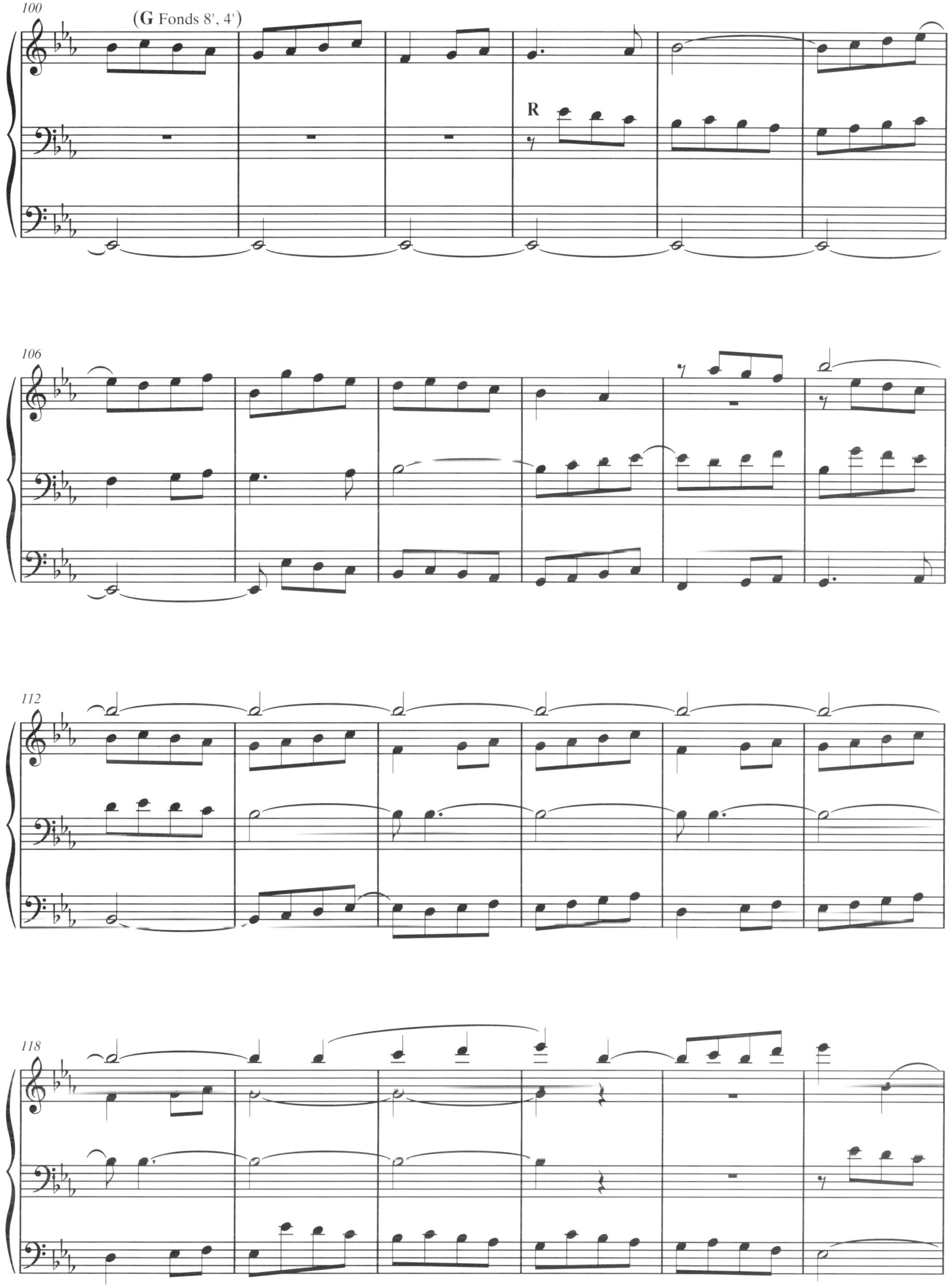
100
(G Fonds 8', 4')
R
106
112
118

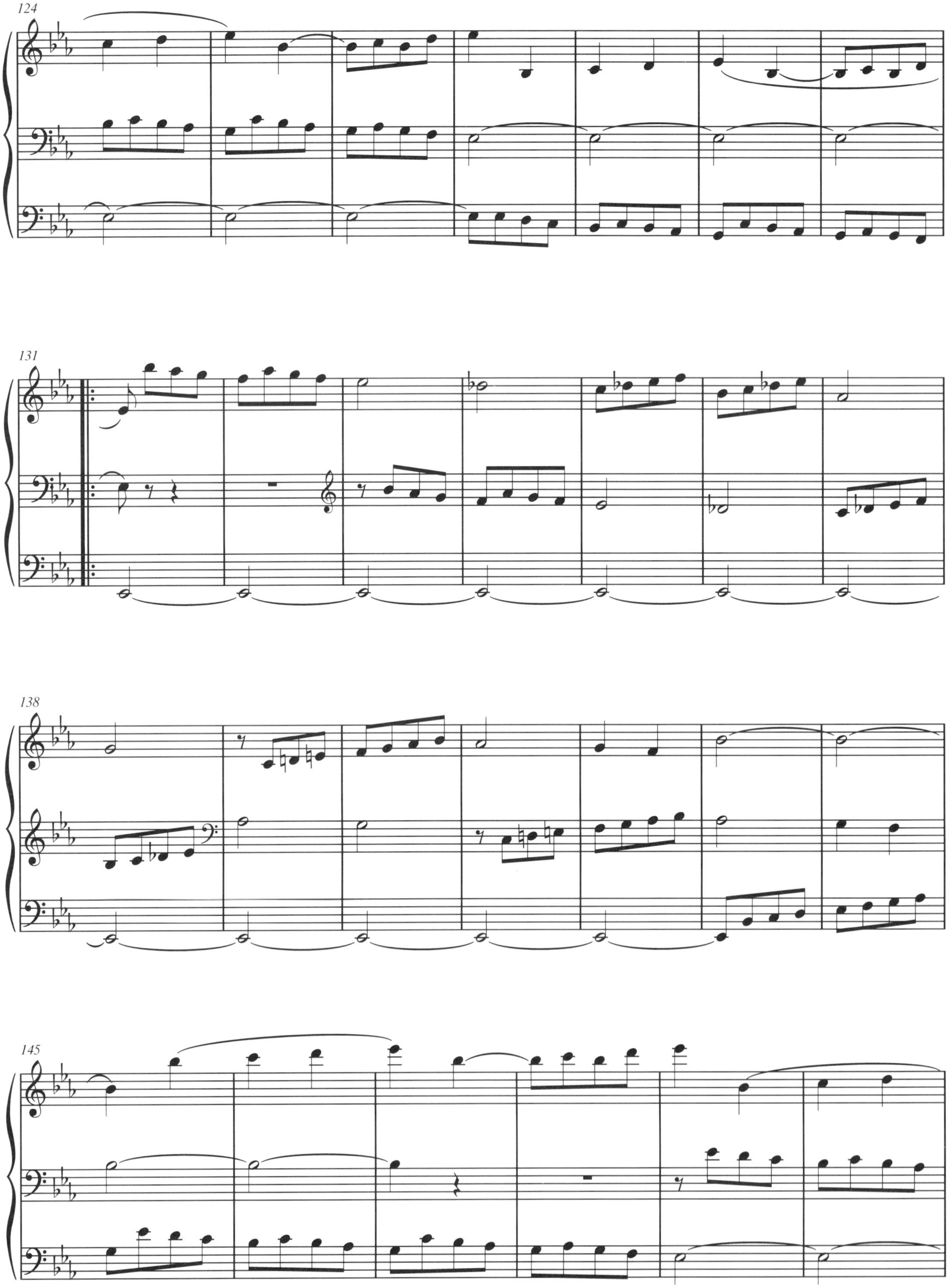
124
131
138
145

151
157
GR
163
cresc.
poco
a
poco
169
e
ritard.
a tempo
G Anches [8', 4', Cornet]
GPR
[f]

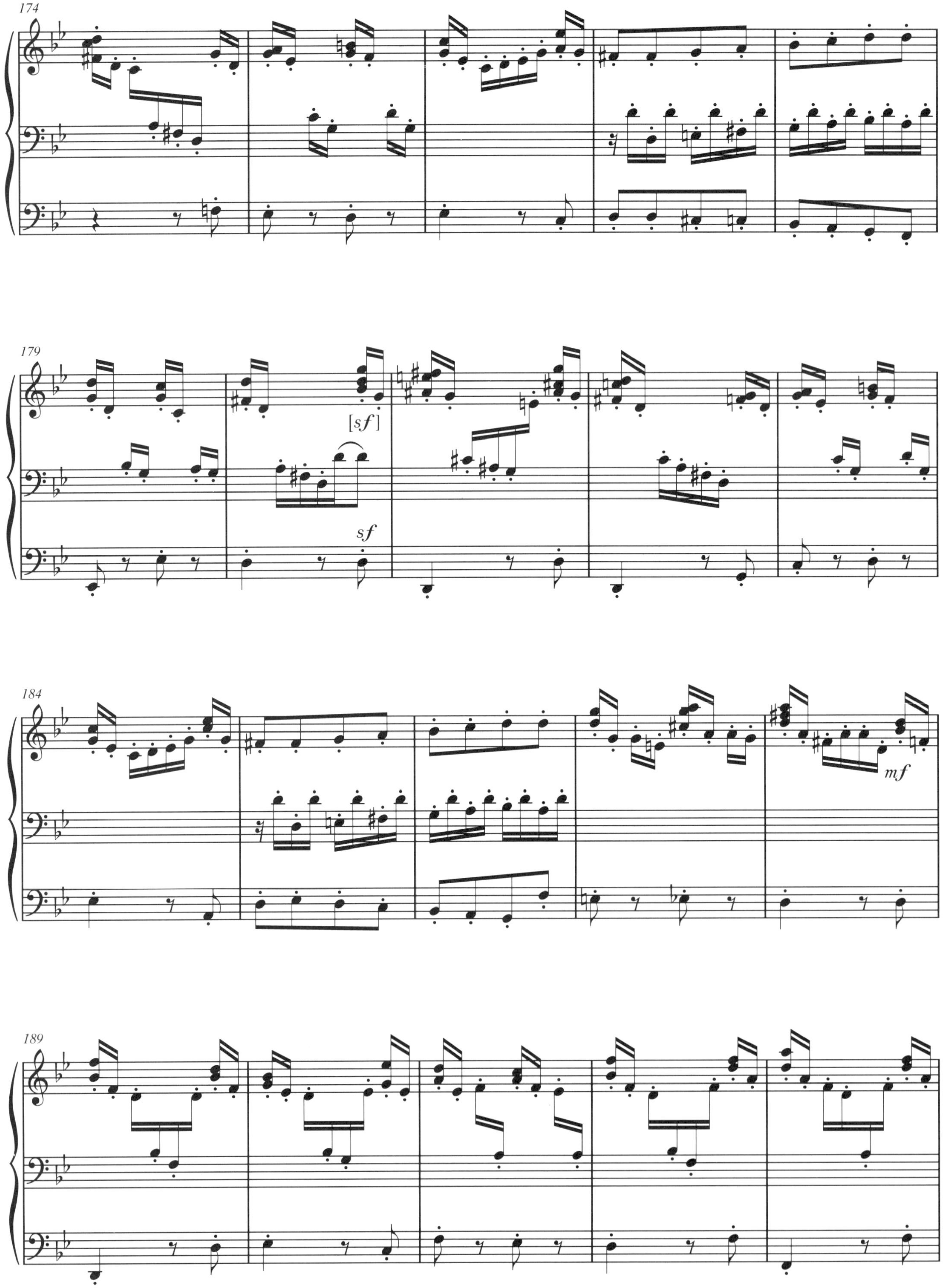
174
179
[sf]
sf
184
mf
189

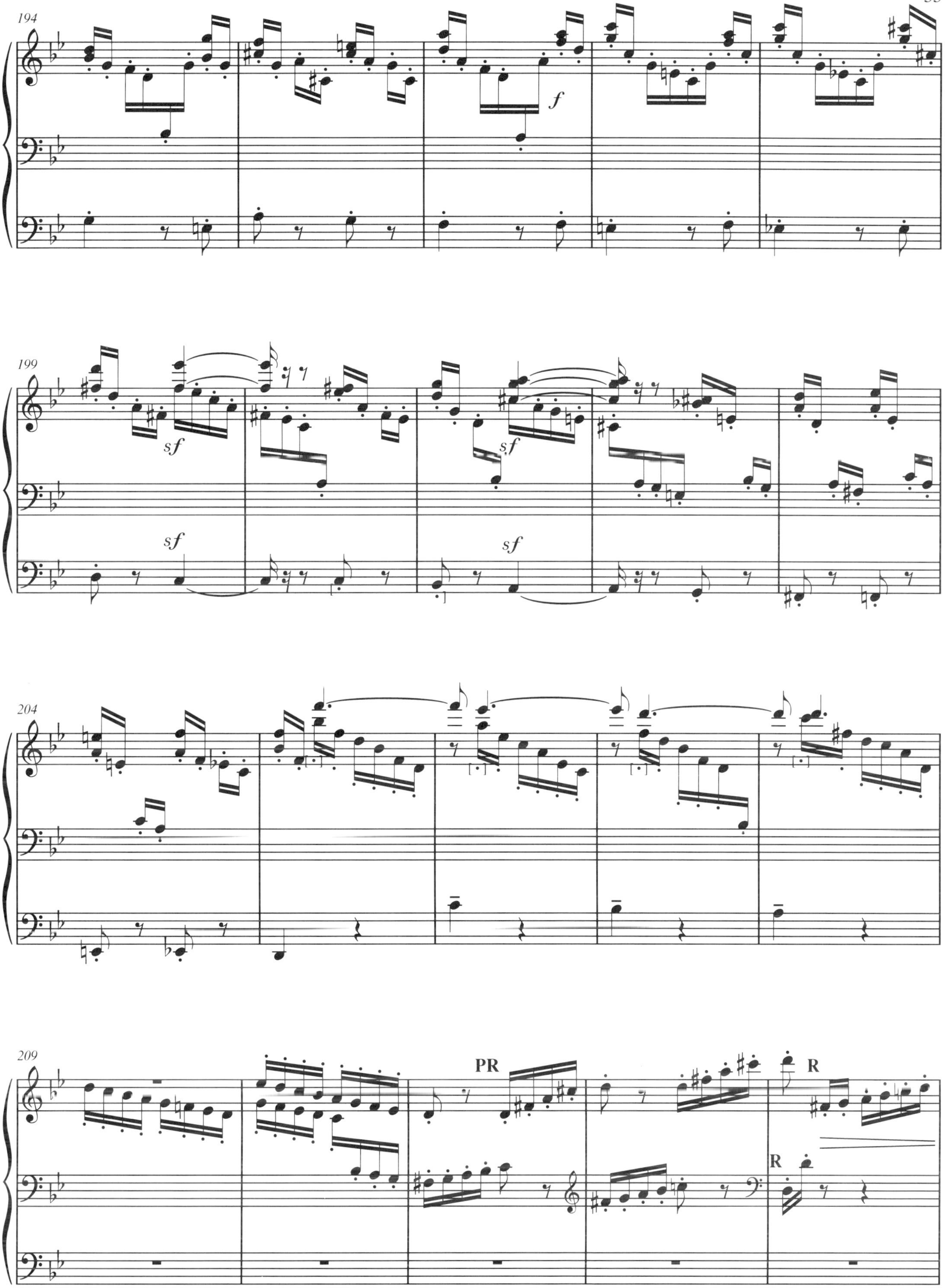
194
f
199
sf
sf
sf
sf
204
209
PR
R
R

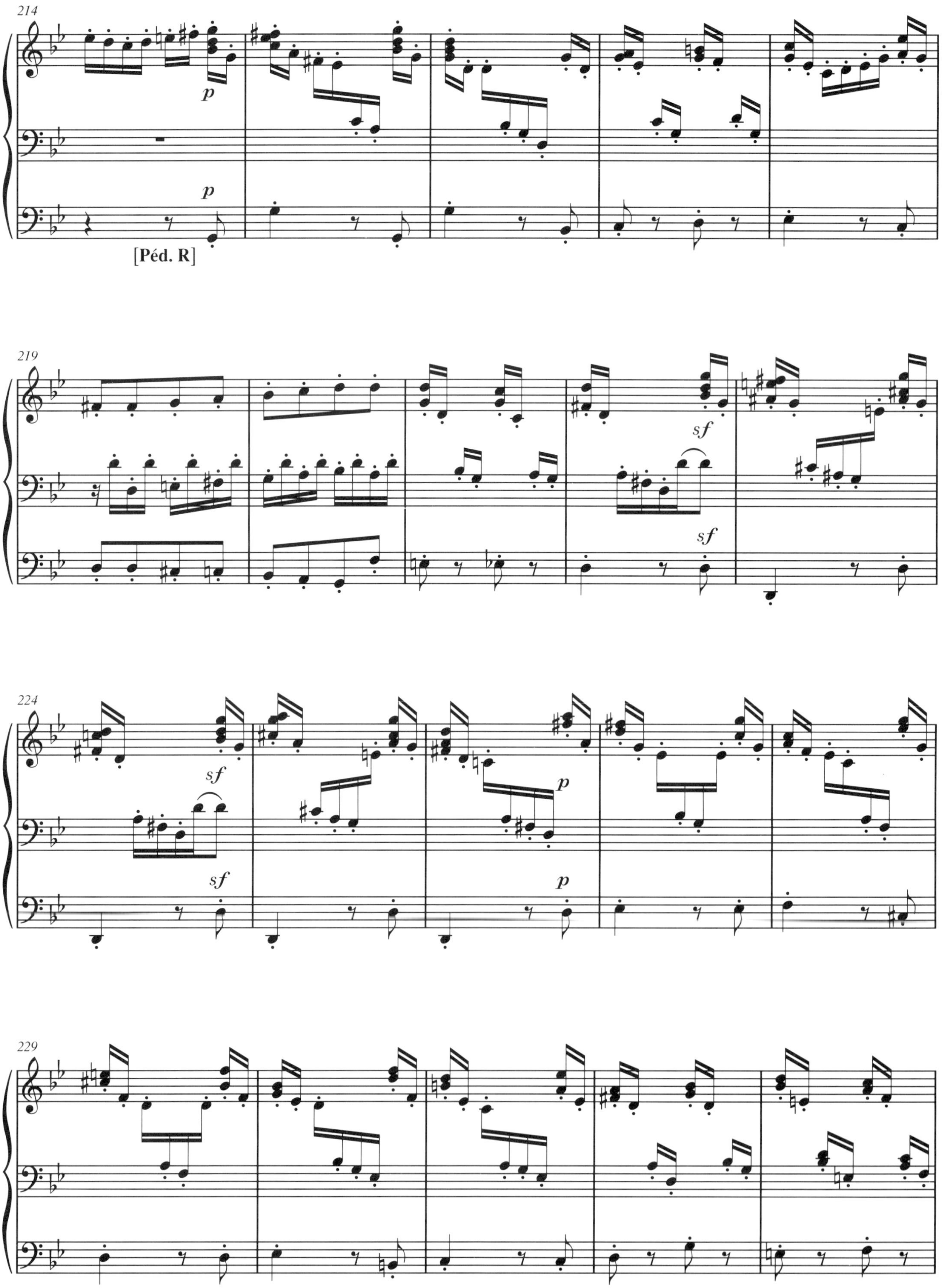
214
p
p
[Péd. R]
219
sf
sf
224
sf
sf
p
p
229

234
pp
pp
239
cresc.
cresc.
GPR
f
f
PR
[Péd. GPR]
244
GPR
PR
249
GPR
PR
GPR
PR
GPR

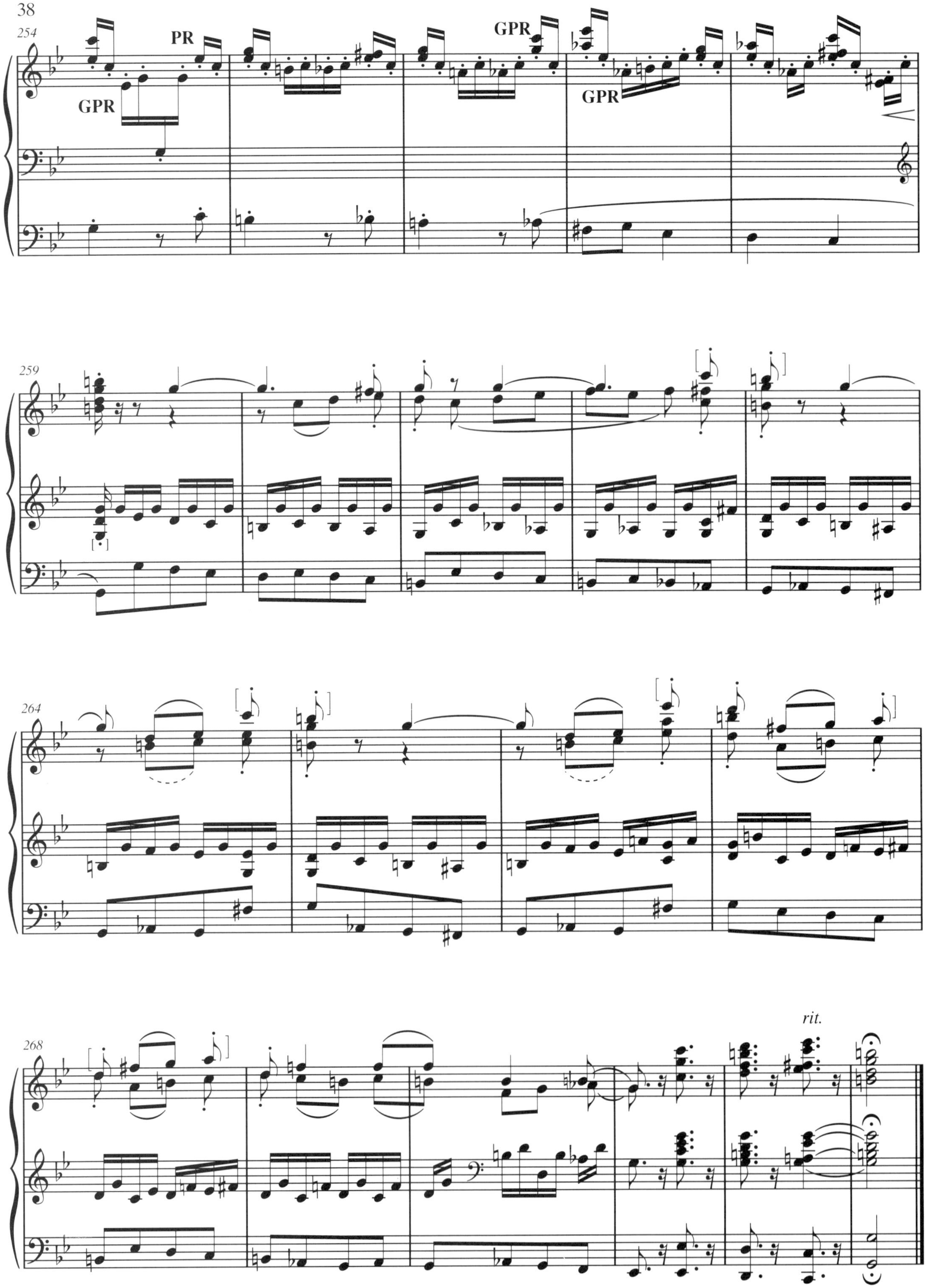
254
PR
GPR
GPR
GPR
259
264
268
rit.

Grand orgue: Flûte 8'
Positif: Montres 16', 8', Prestant [4']
Récit: Hautbois [8']
Pédale: Basses 16', 8'

IV

Cantabile (♩ = 56)

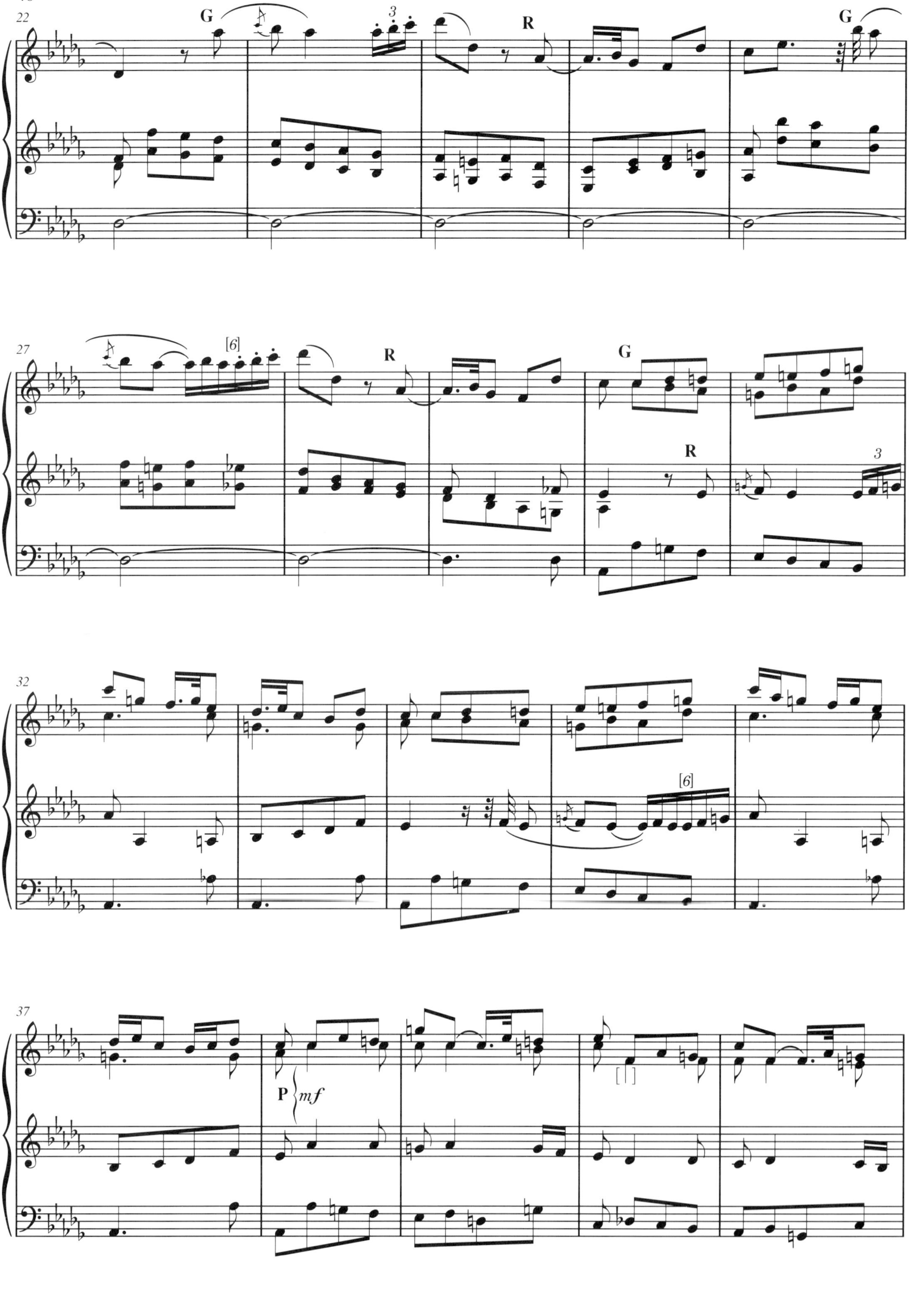
G
R
P
mf

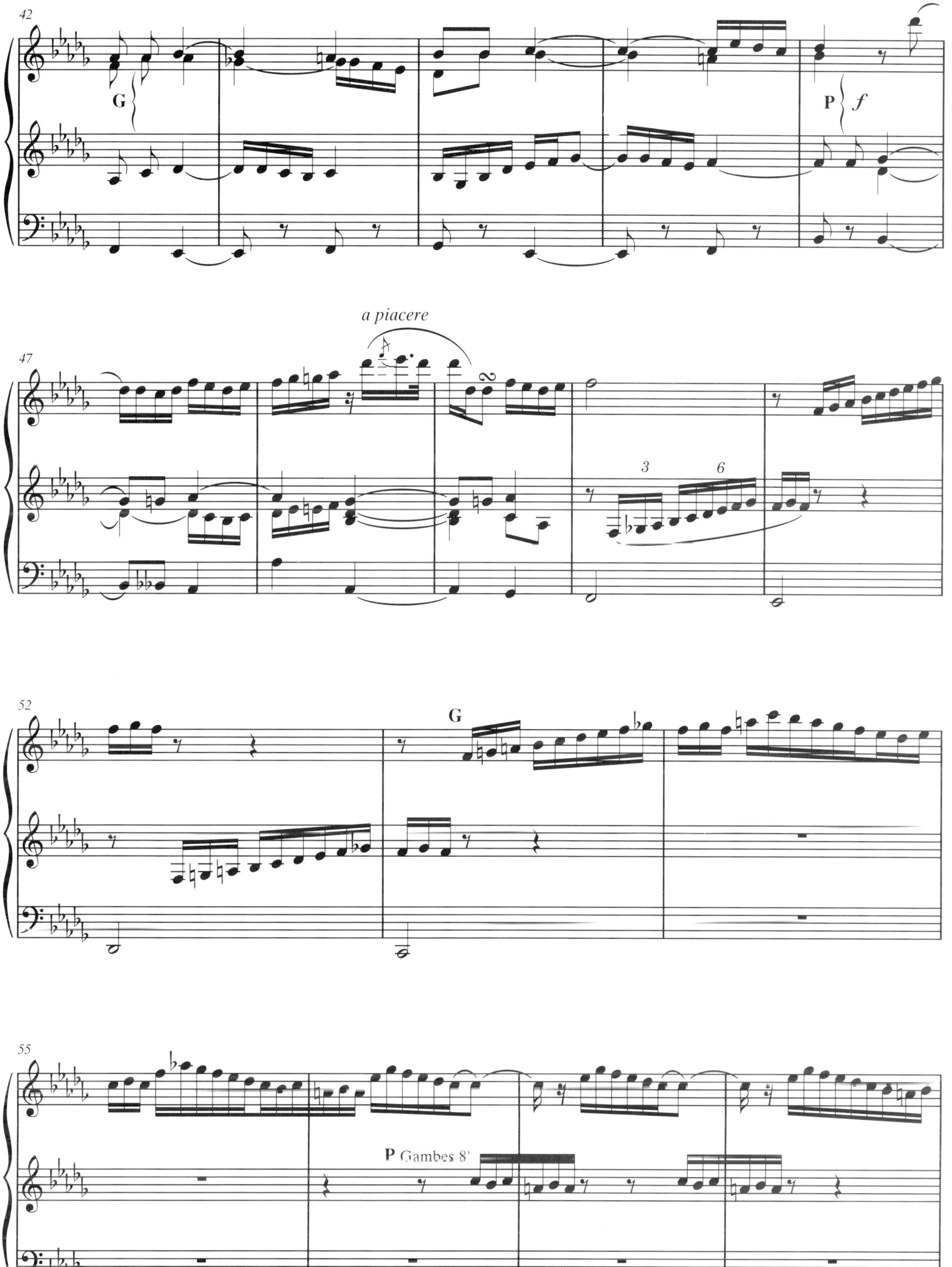
42
G
P
f
47
a piacere
3
6
52
G
55
P Gambes 8'

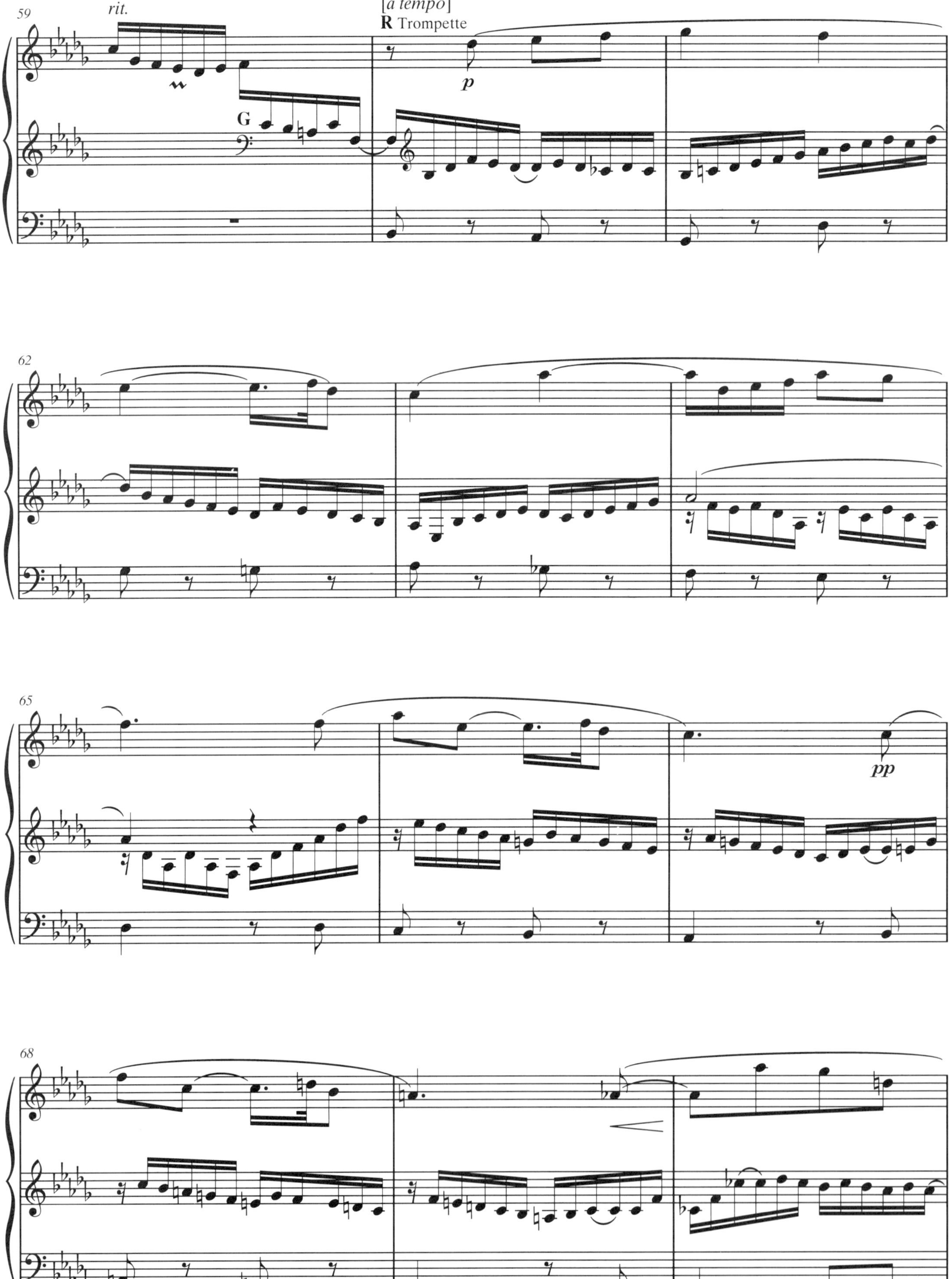
59
rit.
[a tempo]
R Trompette
p
G
62
65
pp
68

43

87
dim.
6
6
pp
(Péd. 16', 8')
94
Più lento
G
R [Gambe 8',] Voix céleste
R
mf
100
riten.
[a tempo]
[6]
106

Grand orgue:
Positif: [Fonds 16', 8', 4',] Anches 16', 8', 4'
Récit:
Pédale: [Fonds 32', 16', 8',] Anches 32', 16', 8'

V. Finale

Vivace ($\mathbf{\textit{d}} = 92$)

[GPR] *fff*

[Péd. GPR]

46

47

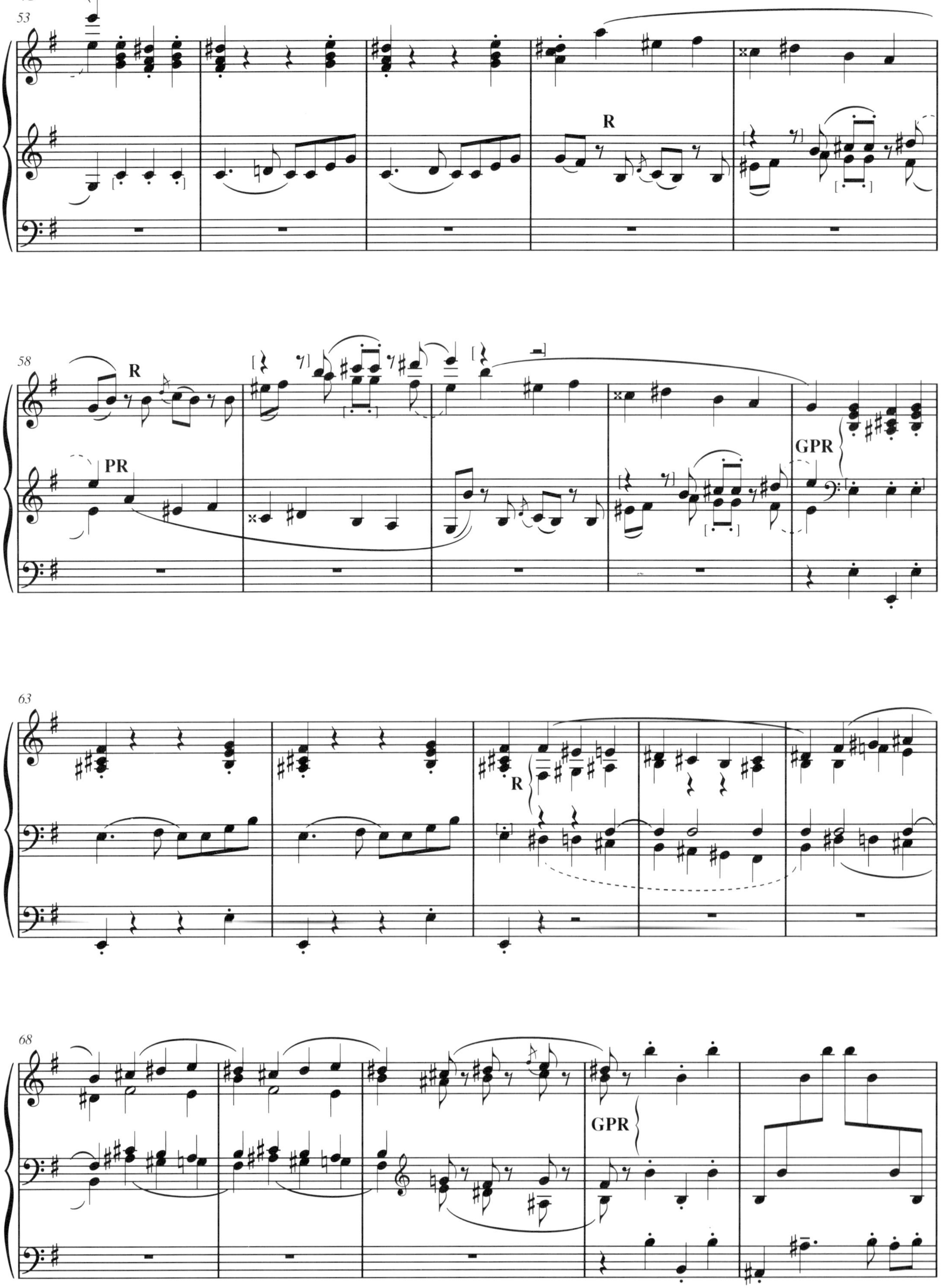
53
R
58
R
PR
GPR
63
R
68
GPR

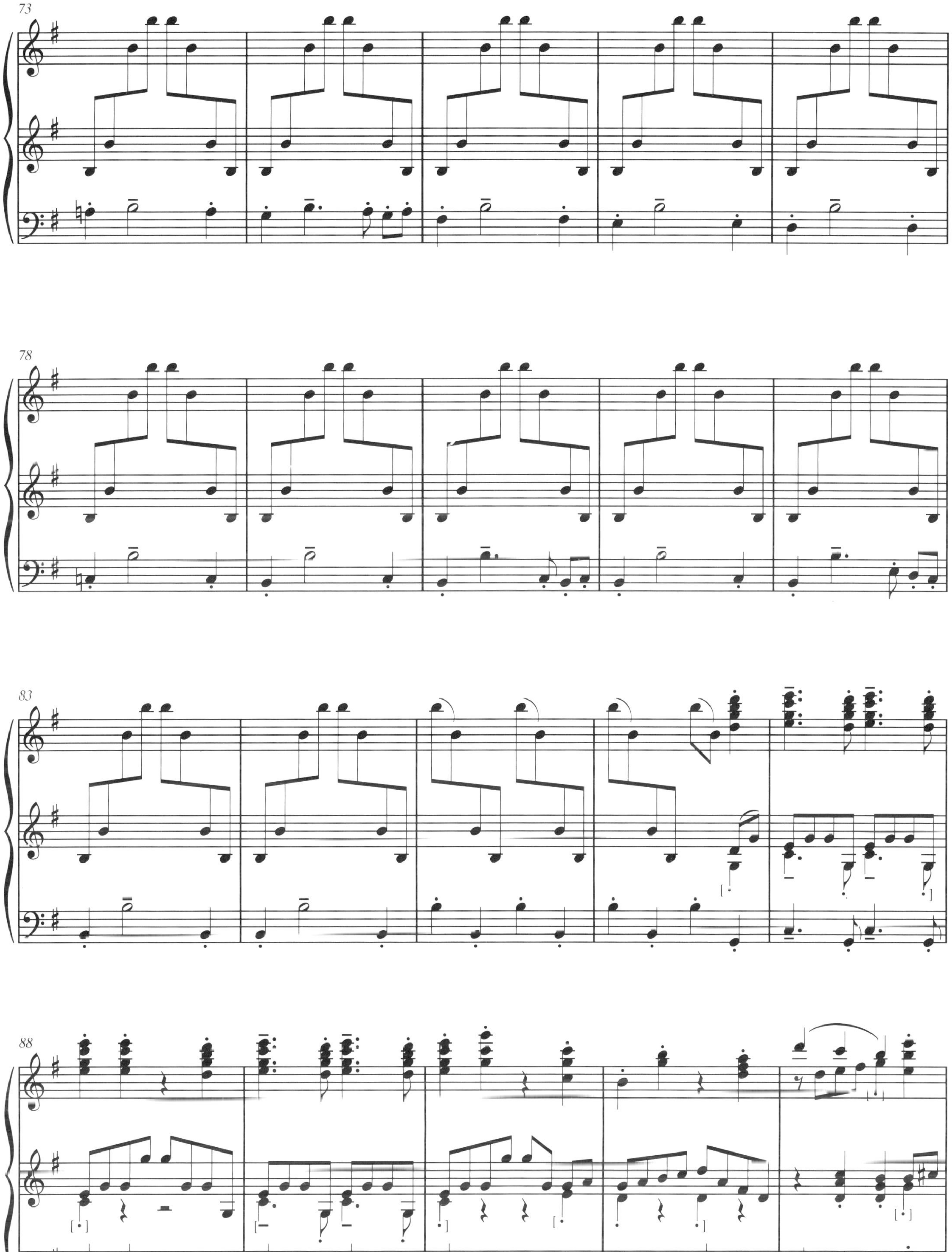
73
78
83
88

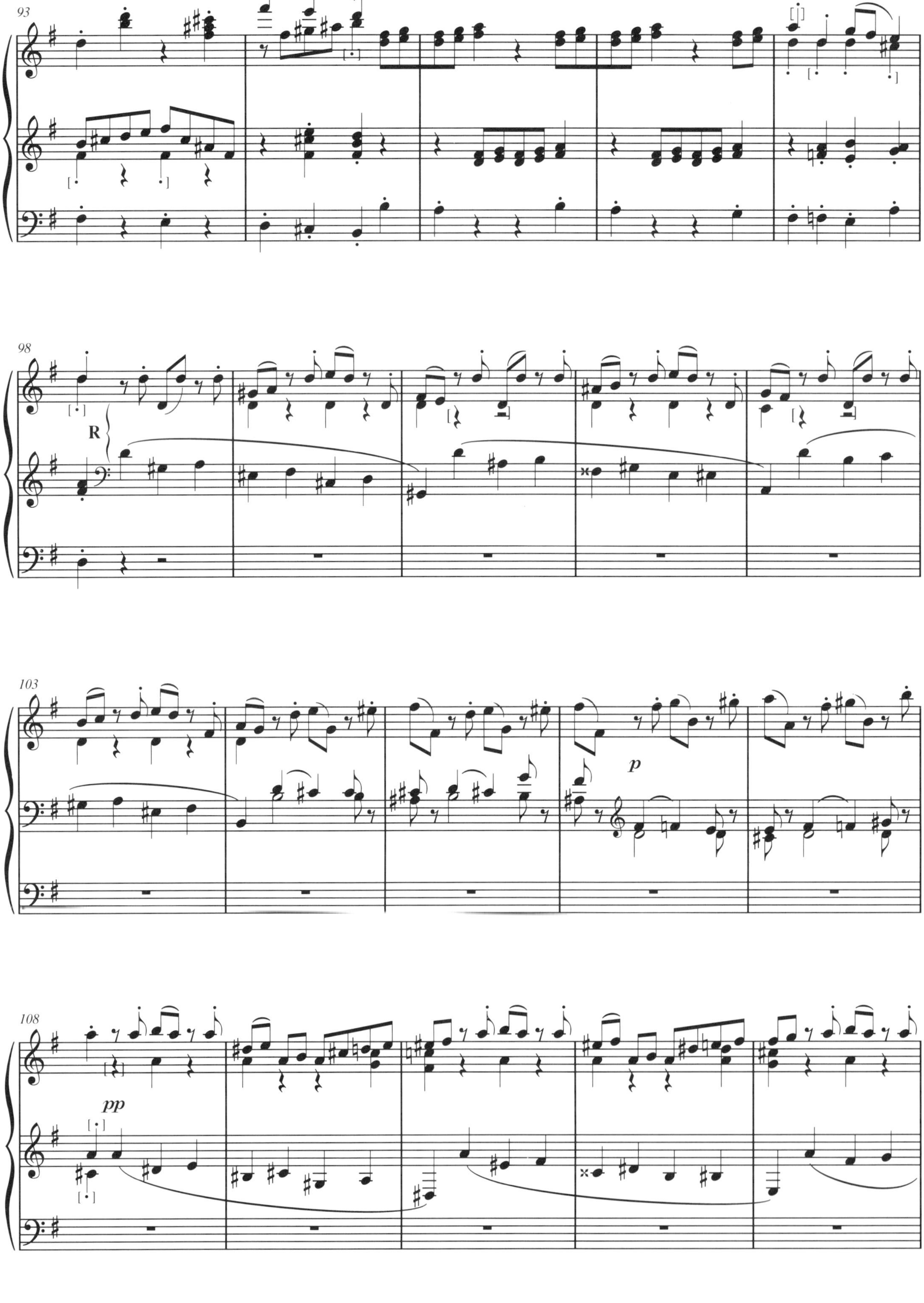
93
98
R
103
p
108
pp

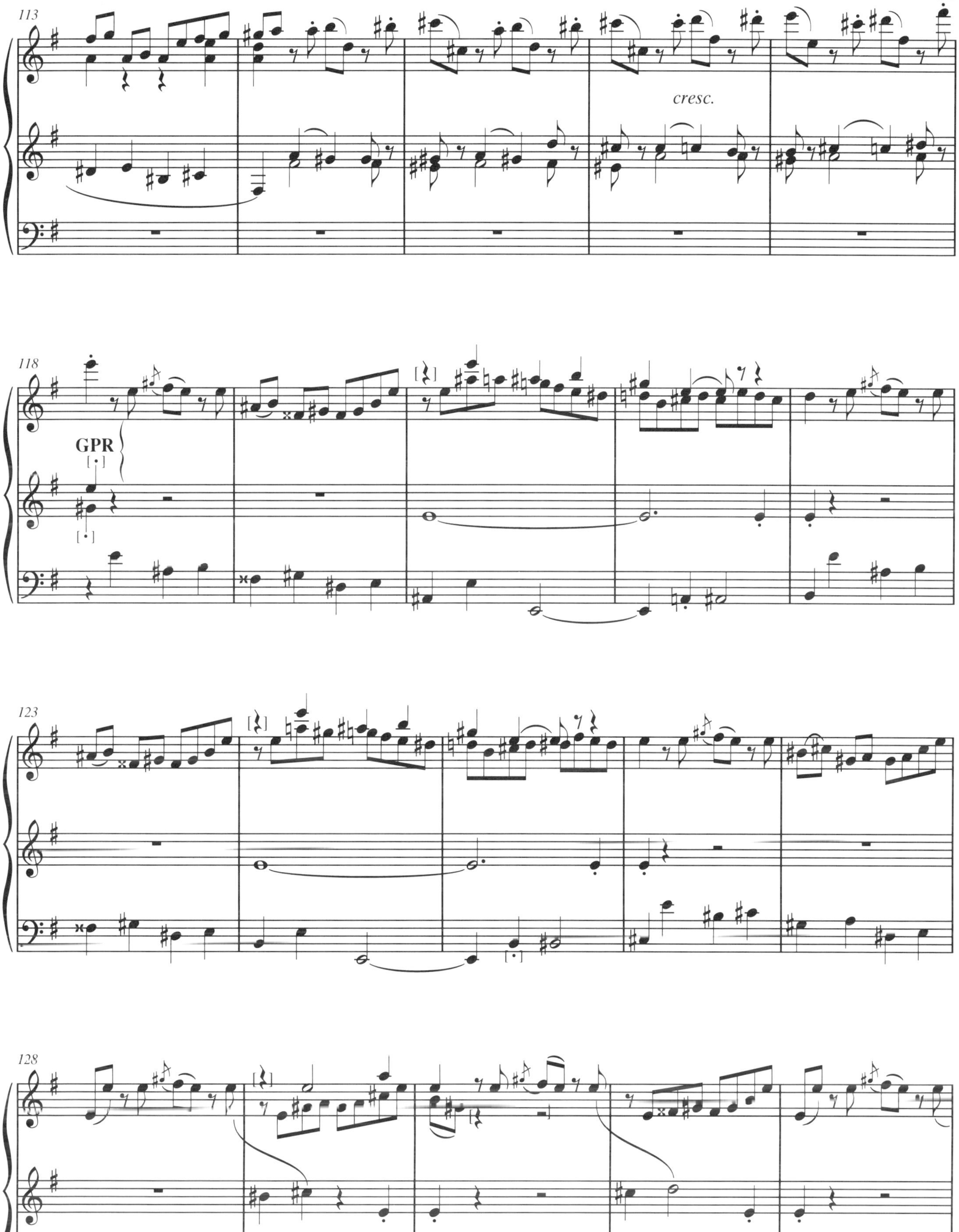
113
cresc.
118
GPR
123
128

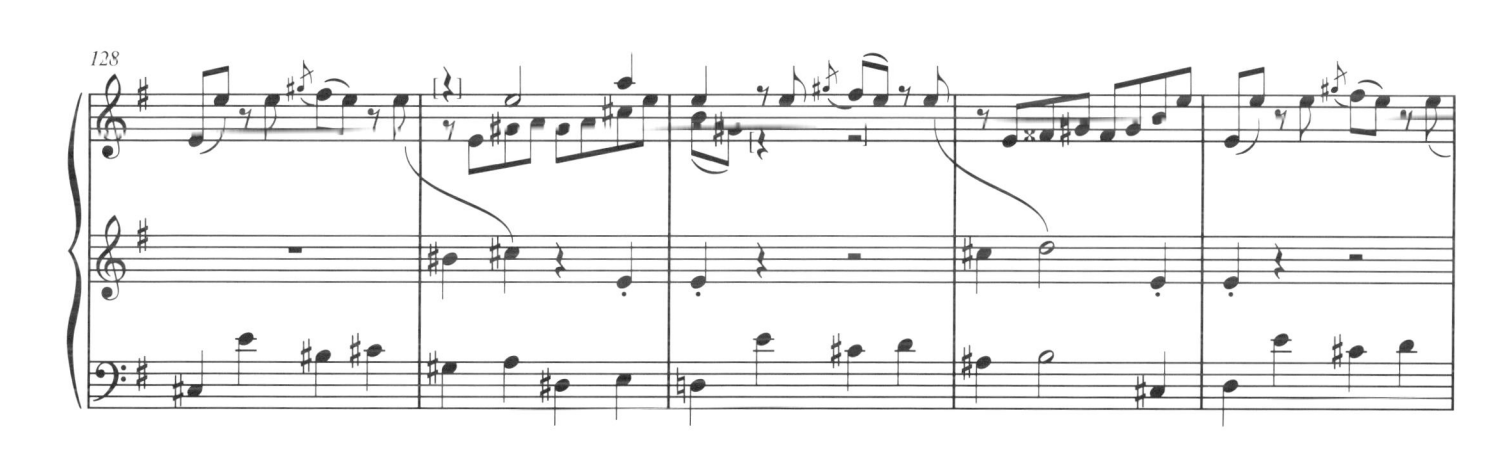

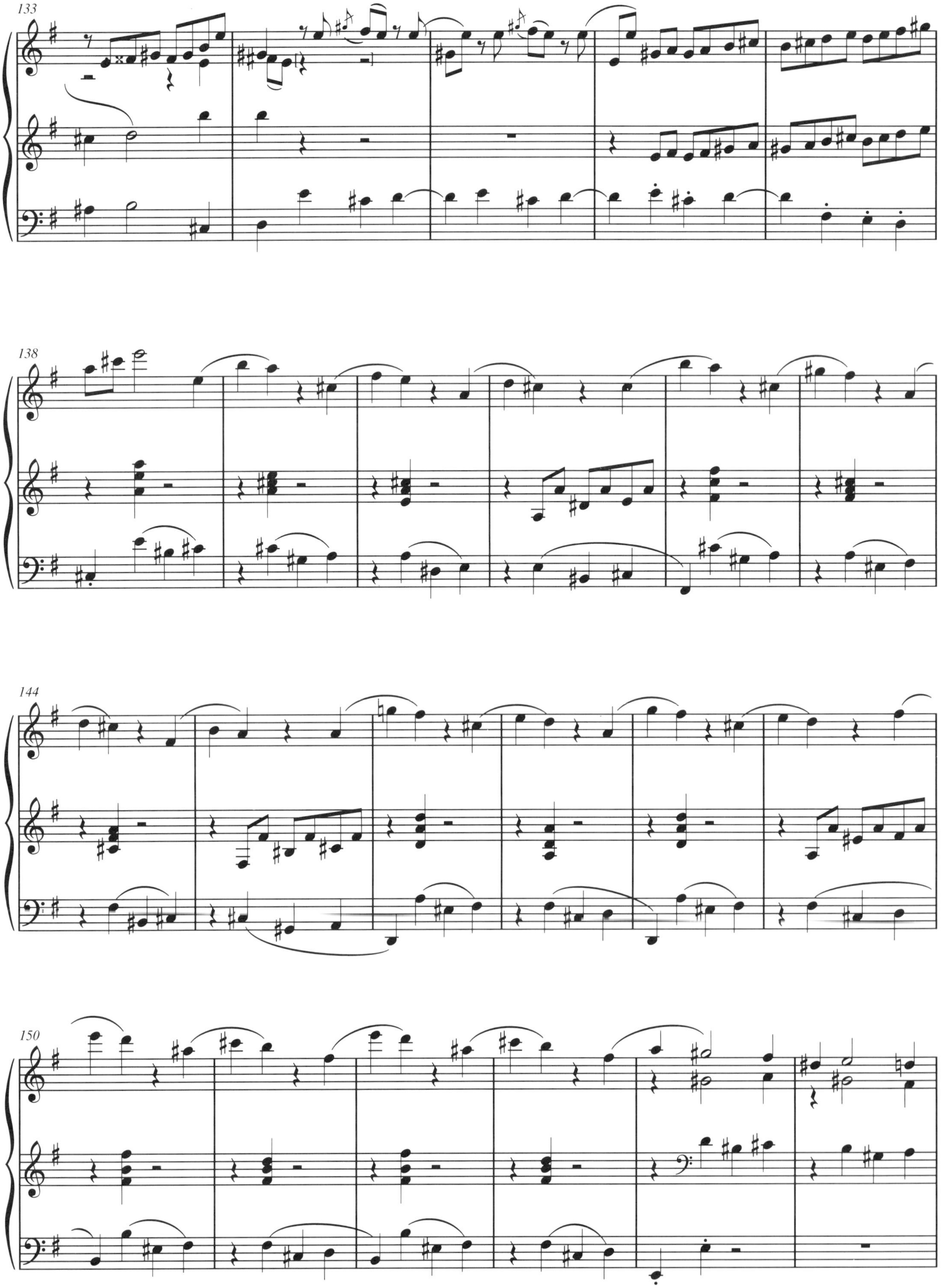
133
138
144
150

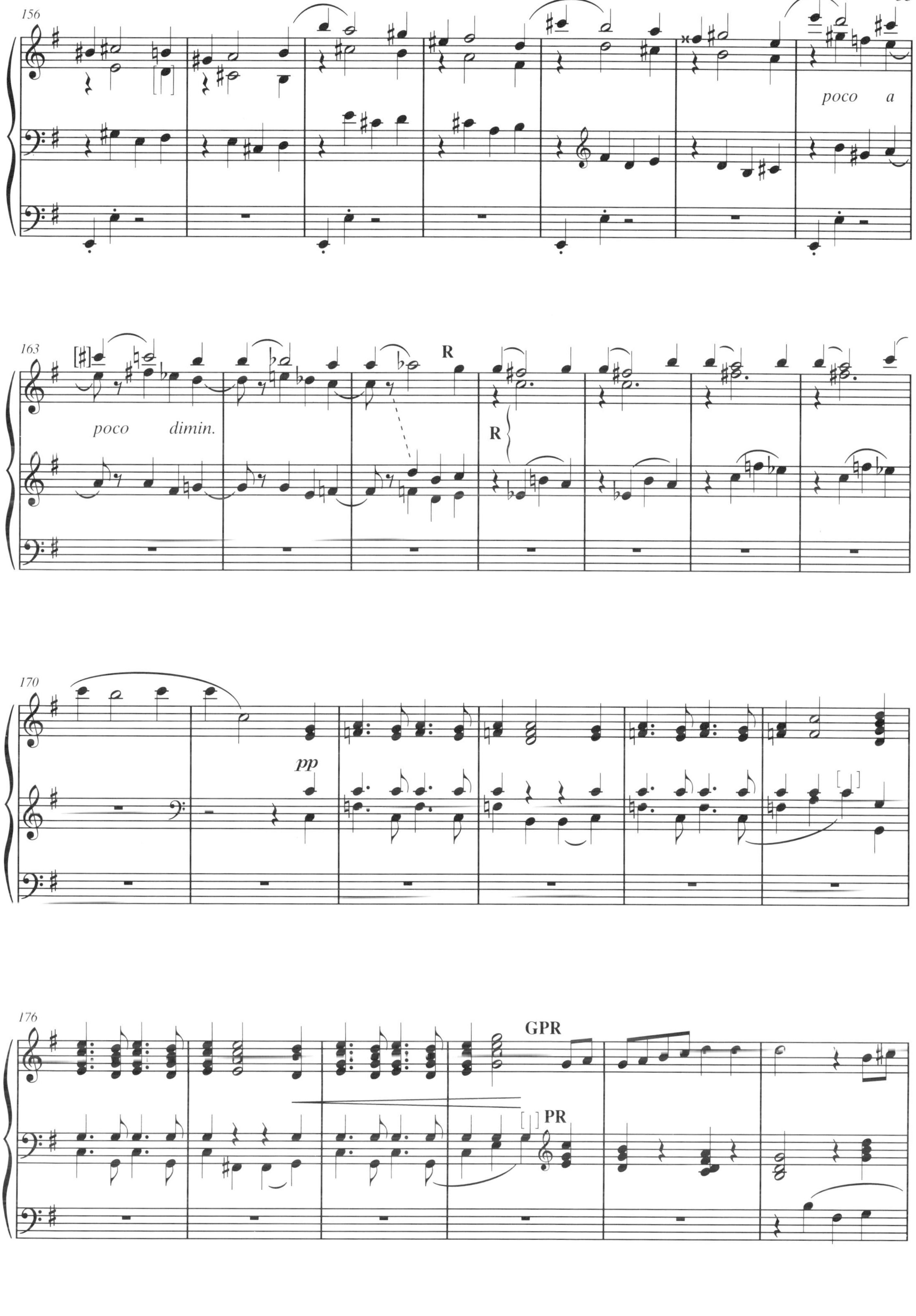
156
poco a
163
poco dimin.
R
R
170
pp
176
GPR
PR

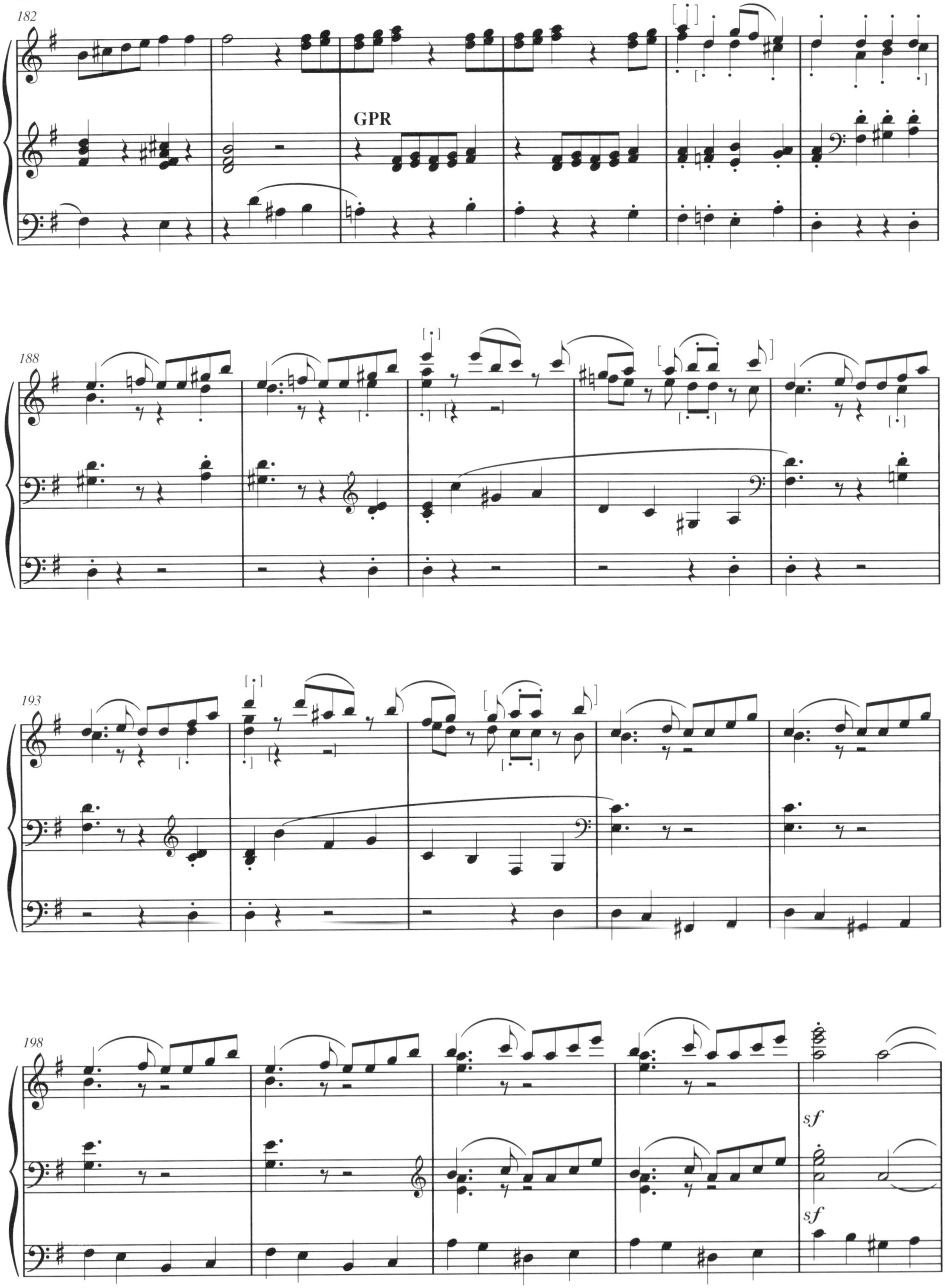
182
GPR
188
193
198
sf
sf

55

228
rit.
più mosso
sf
sf
sempre staccato
234
239
tr
sf
244
tr
tr
tr
Adagio
tr
rit.
sf
sf
sf
sf
3
3

Appendix 1

I

Edition *A'*, Versions *B/B'* and *C'/D*, Mm. 123–31*

*Edition *A'*, versions *B/B'* and *C'/D*, mm. 123 and 131 = edition *E*, mm. 123 and 131.

Appendix 2
III. Intermezzo

Edition *A′*, Mm. 81–100, 253–73*

*Edition *A′*, mm. 81, 100, and 253 = edition *E*, m. 81, 100, and 253.

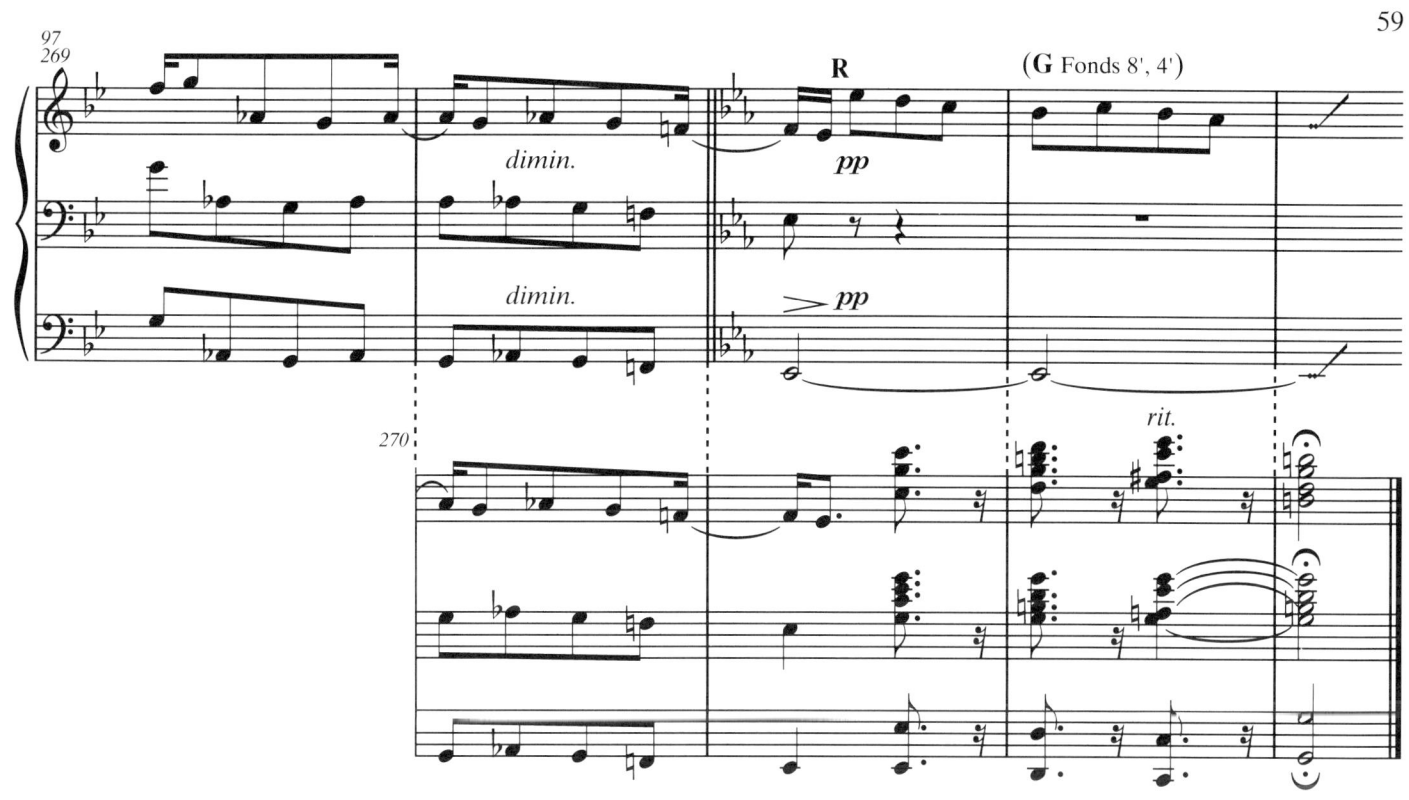

Appendix 3
III. Intermezzo
Edition *B*, Mm. 81–100, 253–73*

*Edition *B*, mm. 81, 100, and 253 = edition *E*, mm. 81, 100, and 253.

*Mm. 267–68, 268–69: see Critical Commentary, "Appendix 3."

Appendix 4
III. Intermezzo

Version *C'/D*, Mm. 87–96, 259–68*

*Version *C'/D*, mm. 87, 96, 259, and 268 = edition *E*, mm. 87, 96, 259, and 268.

4765